Thieves
&
Kings

ISBN: 0-9681025-3-0

Printed in Canada

I would like to thank *Tara S. Wells* for her regular assistance in editing the
pages of *Thieves & Kings, Carson Court* for helping to solve various writing
problems, and *Anthony Davis* for providing the voice of the *'Dark One'* on
page 5; he has my permission to reprint that page as it appears, size
notwithstanding.

I Box Publishing welcomes any comments or questions at the
above address, and may publish/answer them in the letters
pages of the on-going comic book series, available at finer
comic shops everywhere.

Introduction

Welcome to the *Shadow Book.* Or as I like to think of it, the *Autumn Book.*

People have been asking me now for nearly three years, "What color will the next one be?" And for a long while, I thought I was going to surprise everybody by giving it a proper title instead, and that the title would be, *"The Queen of Trolls,"* which I felt had a wonderfully evocative ring and would make Katara seem all the more startling and amazing when she finally swept back into the story. As it turned out though, no matter how much planning one does, (or how startling and amazing Katara happens to be), a story knows itself best in the end. As it turns out, this book belongs heart and soul, to Soracia.

And Autumn is Soracia's season. The first three books, written and drawn during a height of turmoil and wonder in the comics industry, *felt* like summertime. Hot and bright and alive. And exhausting. I thought it was fitting that the season should change. . .

Autumn, incidentally, is my favorite season of the year. While I type this out, the Fall is happing right outside my window. Cool and bright, leaves turned crispy cling to my big sweater when I walk along the train tracks which cut an East and West swath of tangled wilderness a short walk from my house. . . The train company put up fences to stop people from hiking through the tall grass and trees which hide from the rest of the metropolis two sets of freight tracks and a scruffy dirt road. —Something about keeping people from getting hit by trains, I'm told. And from launching lawsuits. Phooey, and fair enough, I say. I think it's important for people to live side by side with impassive dangers of the sort. Like rivers and climbing apparatuses in school yards which knock out a couple of teeth every year. Two hundred kids learn more about safety from one broken collar bone than they do from a year's worth of boring tutorials. —Not that teaching is in any way unnecessary, but I know that most of what I have learned about life was done simply by watching the odd disaster or two unfold around me. Thankfully, for as long as there have been walls surrounding the hidden places, people have been cutting and bending the heavy gauge wire of chain link fences into treacherous, rusty holes through which people can duck if they dare. Life is on the other side, among the weeds and the rails.

I don't know who it is that goes about making the holes in all those chain link fences, but whoever they are, I wish them well! Walking along earth and root, taking short-cuts through over-grown ravines, I feel grateful whenever I glance through a hole in the leaves or peer down from a forbidden train bridge to see cars and grim pedestrians lined up at red lights waiting for their turns to use the tarmac; The King's Highway. One day perhaps I will invest in a pair of bolt cutters to add to the on-going work of keeping the secret rabbit trails maintained; The Thieve's Road, (if you'll pardon such a thudding comparison.)

I currently live in an eighty year-old house in a patch of Toronto known as Little Portugal. Aside from the bright kitsch front yards and the blustery Portugese spoken across the streets between old neighbors, living in Little Portugal means that I have thick and glorious grape vines with plump fruit growing in a canopy over a third of my rustic little back yard. (Rustic, meaning that the garage needs to be demolished and rebuilt from the ground up. It has that sagging barn look which is so popular among landscape artists. Being an artist, though, I enjoy it just fine. And anyway, there's a family of feral cats which lives there and keeps me company from time to time.)

In that backyard, I have learned to sit during the warm months out under the shade of those grape leaves in a swinging canvas chair, musing and writing and sketching in great peace. I share the house with two dashing girls and a landlord who lives in the basement and who bounds up the stairs to meet me when we're both in the house at the same time so that we can make meals together and talk about stuff. The four of us have been living here for nearly a year and a half now, which seems quite impossible. I remember when a year meant a period of time which was *long!* Time is rushing by these days.

I suspect that it won't be long before our little family is broken up as one or more of us are called away to attend to the errands and adventures which life both offers and demands. I hope I'll be staying in this beautiful little house for at least another year, but we'll have to see. I shiver at the thought of having to pack everything up and drag my heavy drafting board anywhere. It's just not comfortable, and I've already done it a few times more than I have wanted these last few years. If I wasn't a cartoonist I'd be able to move much more lightly! All those books and computer bits and that drafting board. . . Sheesh! You'd think that I could get by with a note pad, some inks, and a back pack stuffed with jeans and shirts. And maybe a portable computer.

Hm. Come to think of it. . .

I love travel and it has been far too long. —And I confess, having the ability to pick up and move on very short notice has always been an attractive thought. My father once took me aside and told me this: "Mark, you're what? About thirty?" "Yeah, Dad. Thirty." "Well, you're not married and you have no children. You have very little responsibility and a great deal of freedom. That's worth considering."

I don't know exactly what his point was, and I'm not sure he did either, but the words stuck with me for a long while.

It was really nice living in a proper apartment two years back with a smart and pretty girlfriend; with grown up furniture and shelves and nick-knacks. Domestic and distracting, but good. And it has also been pleasant living with room mates. I keep meeting the most charming people! —And sharing space with Tara Jenkins, my cartoonist friend way back in the beginning; that was fun and it was exactly what I needed at the time, (when eating & breathing comics was the most important thing in the world!) But that was several years ago now, and there's a whole lot of the world which I've not yet explored. Ducking under the vandalized edges of chain link fences designed to keep people from walking the secret paths where milkweed and raspberries grow. . . That has a way of reminding me of something forgotten. . .

I have a friend with family in the Carribean. I know people who have friends in Costa Rica. Perhaps I'll go to Central America and try drawing there for a while. Where better to write about winter than in a place where such a thing as snow can only be imagined? And maybe when I come home again, I'll be able to write about the tropics. And pirates.

We'll see.

Take care and enjoy this book. It has been a true labor of both sweat and love, and I am very pleased with how it has turned out. I hope you will be as well!

Mark Oakley
Toronto, Canada
October, 2001

RUBEL IS GOING TO GET HIMSELF **KILLED** IF HE'S NOT CAREFUL!

THE SHADOW LADY IS **CRAZY!**

QUINTON SAID SHE'S NOT SO BAD. SHE'S JUST HAD A ROUGH TIME OF IT.

THAT'S WHAT **HE** SAYS.

WHY IS IT SO WRONG FOR HER TO LOVE RUBEL?

SHE'S LIKE A **MILLION** YEARS OLD!!

AND SHE CAN KILL PEOPLE JUST BY **LOOKING** AT THEM!

SHE'S DONE ALL KINDS OF BAD THINGS TO RUBEL. SHE GOT HIM SHOT AND SHE POISONED HIM. —AND SHE WASN'T EVEN **ANGRY!**

NO...

WHAT IF SHE EVER GETS **ANGRY** WITH HIM? —EVER THINK OF THAT?

BUT RUBEL IS **STRONG**

I THINK HE'S PROBABLY THE ONLY ONE WHO **COULD** DEAL WITH HER. AND ANYWAY, LOVE MAKES YOU DO CRAZY THINGS.

EXACTLY!

THAT'S WHAT I'M TALKING ABOUT! THAT'S WHY YOU SHOULDN'T GET MIXED UP IN IT!

QUINTON IS AN IDIOT, BUT AT LEAST HE GOT **THAT** RIGHT.

HE NEVER FALLS IN LOVE.

THAT'S WHAT SCARES ME.

QUINTON HAS ALL THESE BIG PLANS FOR ME, AND IT'S LIKE HE'S STARTED MAKING THEM COME TRUE

HE'S **SO** POWERFUL! —PEOPLE DON'T REALIZE IT, AND I'M ONLY JUST STARTING TO, BUT HE'S **REALLY** POWERFUL!

AND WHAT IF HE DOESN'T WANT ME TO FALL IN **LOVE?**

WHAT IF HE EXPECTS ME TO BE LIKE HIM?

I DON'T WANT TO NOT FALL IN LOVE!

WHAT IF I MEET SOMEONE? WHAT HAPPENS THEN?

WELL..., YOU'VE GOT A LOT OF TIME TO WORRY ABOUT IT IN. —YOU'RE STILL YOUNG.

YEAH...

I GUESS

Chapter 1

MY LADY.

LOCUMIRE.

THE MINISTERS INFORM ME THAT YOU HAVE BEEN *TROUBLED.*

IT HAS BEEN... *DIFFICULT* OF LATE.

YES. I'M SURE IT HAS.

PERHAPS QUINTON MADE HIM WELL ENOUGH TO SEE THROUGH THIS INFERNAL FOG WHICH SURROUNDS ME.

NONESENSE.

YOU TOOK HIM TO THE *DRAGON'S DREAM.*

YOU USE THE GARDEN LIKE A DRUG. AND THAT IS WHERE QUINTON'S THIEF FELL IN LOVE WITH YOU.

REALLY!

I HAVE SPENT A THOUSAND YEARS KNOWING THE MINDS OF LOVELORN GIRLS.

BUT YOU MUST KNOW IT WILL NOT LAST.

THE PERSON YOU ARE IN THE GARDEN IS ONLY ROGUE'S DREAM OF YOU, AND YOU TRICKED ROGUE LONG AGO INTO THINKING YOU WERE A NAIVE, FORGIVING CREATURE.

WE BOTH KNOW YOUR **TRUE** FEELINGS!

JUST BECAUSE A SILLY DRAGON CANNOT SEE THE TRUTH, DOESN'T MEAN IT ISN'T THERE. —THE ANGRY PARTS OF YOUR SOUL ARE YOURS FOREVER; THEY ARE NOT A SET OF CHAINS A THIEF CAN UNLOCK.

I KNOW YOU HAVE BEEN THINKING THAT RECENTLY.

THESE LONG YEARS MAKE IT EASY TO FORGET SUCH THINGS.

BUT I AM HERE TO REMIND YOU WHEN YOU ARE BEING FOOLISH.

IT IS JUST QUINTON'S TRICK OF THE MIND PLAYING UPON YOU.

YOU MUST REALIZE BY NOW THAT THERE IS ONLY ONE TRUE SALVATION.

NOTHING GOOD CAN SPRING FROM SUCH HATERED.

TSK.

HATERED IS A NATURAL EMOTION.

IT IS PERFECTLY NORMAL TO BE REPULSED BY THE GROTESQUE AND DEFORMED. —THE *STUPID.*

AUG!

THINGS ARE CHANGING MORE THAN YOU REALIZE, SHADOW.

LEHANNA. KIMITHIN. WOULD YOU COME HERE PLEASE.

HAVE YOU FETCHED THE BOTTLE?

YES MADAME.

I KNEW SHE WOULD BE BOLD.

I WANT TO KNOW IF IT'S TRUE THAT SHE KISSED HER THIEF LAST NIGHT AND FRIGHTENED HIM AWAY.

IT IS DIFFICULT FOR THOSE WHO ONCE HELD HIGH STATIONS TO ACCEPT SUBSERVIENCE.

DOES SHE KNOW ABOUT THE PLAN?

GIRLS, THESE QUESTIONS ARE NOT APPROPRIATE RIGHT NOW.

OF COURSE, MADAME. FORGIVE US.

IT'S JUST THAT THE SHADOW WOMAN IS A RARE CURIOSITY.

WHAT PLAN?

YOU DON'T MEAN TO CART OUT THE OLD RUDGAR THEORUM AGAIN, DO YOU?

PHAW!

DON'T THE MINISTERS HAVE EVEN THE COMMON GRACE TO AT LEAST TRY TO LEARN FROM ABJECT FAILURE?

THAT'S NOT FOR YOU TO WORRY ABOUT.

YOU FOUND HIM AT LAST.

SO THAT'S WHY YOU CALLED ME HERE.

I THOUGHT YOUR MESSENGER SEEMED A LITTLE MORE ANXIOUS THAN USUAL.

AND YOU WANT ME TO UNSEAL IT FOR YOU?

HEH.

OH, CONGRATULATIONS.

YOU WANT JURID?

FINE.

JUST REMEMBER; YOU HAVE NEVER SEEN THE DAWN-SWALLOWER AT HIS FULLEST EBB.

SIGH

-AND DESPITE ALL YOU HAVE ACHIEVED IN THIS LAST MILLENIUM...

YOU ARE STILL A MORTAL.

KAS

HAAHAH!...

TOOMP

JURID!

HHUHAH

HELLO, AGAIN! YOU HAVE BEEN TRAPPED IN DREAMS AND IMAGES FOR A LONG TIME, BEAST.

WELCOME TO OCEANSENO!

HUHHH

AND HEAR ME! THE RED SORCERESS LIVES ON, AND SHE HAS NOT FORGOTTEN YOU! -SHE IS STRONG NOW, IN WAYS WHICH WILL CONFUSE YOU!

SHE CAN DESTROY YOU!

LET THAT BE YOUR GIFT FOR RETURNING!

I GIVE YOU FEAR, LOATHSOME ONE!

BE BOUND WITH IT!

HHHHHH!

SHRIEK

OUR SOULS BURN FOR YOU, MY LADY.

YOUR DUTIES ARE ELSEWHERE, ARMSMEN.

YES, M'LADY!

HOW MANY OF MY HONOR-GUARD ARE HERE IN OCEANSEND?

I HAVE COUNTED SIX SINCE THE PRINCE BROUGHT YOU FORTH.

THERE ARE TWELVE OF US AMONG SIXTY.

FOUR OF THAT SIXTY HAVE BEEN DESTROYED. —ONE ONLY NOW AT MY HAND, AND ANOTHER BY YOUR THIEF.

NONE OF THOSE FOUR WERE OF YOUR PERSONAL GUARD.

GO THEN. GATHER UP THE TWELVE AND LEAVE THE CONFINES OF THE CITY;

SEEK SHELTER IN THE SLEEPING WOOD. —ANNOUNCE YOURSELVES TO THE FOREST AS MY PERSONAL GUARD AND YOU WILL BE GRANTED ASYLUM.

NIETHER THE PRINCE NOR LOCUMIRE HAVE THE STRENGTH YET TO PENETRATE THE WOOD, AND THE MINISTERS ARE NOT YET FOCUSED ENOUGH TO CALL OUT TO YOU, SO YOU WILL BE SAFE FOR A TIME.

BUT DO NOT HARM A SINGLE CREATURE WHILE YOU ARE THERE, OR THE WOOD WILL SWALLOW YOU!

WHEN YOU ARE THERE, POLISH YOUR ARMOR SO THAT THE NICKEL AND GOLD SHINES, AND DYE YOUR CLOAKS WITH THE BLUE-ROSE EMBLEM OF MY OLD HOUSE.

THE WOOD WILL ALLOW YOU THE PLANTS AND CLAYS REQUIRED TO DO THIS.

IN THE MEAN TIME, I WILL TRY TO FIGURE SOMETHING OUT.

IF YOU CATCH SCENT OF MY SISTER, AVOID DETECTION AS BEST YOU CAN.

—I HAVE RECENTLY COME TO BELIEVE THAT SHE IS RAISING AN ARMY IN THE FOREST. IF SHE FINDS YOU, SHE WILL DESTROY YOU.

IF YOU COME ACROSS THE KING, DO NOT ENGAGE HIS FORCES EITHER.

THE WOOD WILL BROOK NO WARRING BENEATH ITS SHELTER.

ONLY THE PRINCESS CAN MAKE WAR; THE FOREST WILL HAVE FALLEN IN LOVE WITH HER BY NOW.

FEAR HER!

BUT WHAT OF YOU, LADY SALINA?

Chapter 2

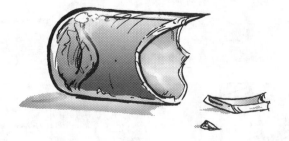

YOUR TEACHER DOESN'T WANT YOU TO **LEARN** ANYTHING! —SHE WANTS TO KEEP KIDS STUPID SO SHE CAN KEEP BILLING THEIR PARENTS!

IT'S OBVIOUSLY A MONEY SCAM!

VARKIAS! SHHH..!

HEATH PORTER! I DON'T KNOW WHAT THAT **OTHER** SCHOOL MIGHT HAVE TAUGHT YOU, BUT THE STUDENTS IN **THIS** SCHOOL DO NOT TALK WHILE WORKING!

YES MA'AM. SORRY.

WHO'S SHE TALKING TO OVER IN THE CORNER..?

SHE'S TALKING TO HERSELF?

OH, SURE! LISTEN TO **HER**.

IF YOU DO WHAT SHE SAYS, YOU'LL BE STUCK HERE FOREVER WHILE SHE MAKES MONEY OFF YOU!

I'M GOING TO GET RUBEL. —HE'LL CUT HER HEAD OFF!

VARKIAS!

SEE? YOU GOT ME INTO TROUBLE ON MY **FIRST** DAY OF SCHOOL!

WOW. YOU WERE ALREADY SITTING IN THE CORNER. NOW YOU'RE OUT IN THE COAT ROOM.

AND IT ISN'T EVEN LUNCH TIME YET!

I CAN'T **BELIEVE** THIS!

WHAT IS JENNY GOING TO SAY?

SHE GOT ME INTO THIS CLASS ON A PERSONAL FAVOR! —SHE'S GOING TO BE REALLY UPSET!

WE COULD TRY TO ESCAPE.

ARE YOU OUT OF YOUR **MIND?!**

GO ON! ASK HER!

WHAT NOW?

YOU ASK HER.

IS IT TRUE THAT YOUR MOTHER IS A PIRATE?

WHAT?

NOT HER MOM, IDIOT! —HER AUNT!

HER AUNT RAN AWAY ON A SAIL-BOAT! —MY NANNY SAID!

IT'S TRUE. RIGHT, NEW KID?

MRS. PORTER'S A PIRATE? YOU'D THINK SHE WOULD HAVE SAID SOMETHING.

I GET THE FEELING THIS IS GOING TO BE A REALLY LONG LUNCH-PERIOD.

WHAT'S THE MATTER? —YOU DEAF!

The other kids at Heath's school didn't know precisely what a prostitute was, having only the vague ideas young people from secure lives often have concerning the complexities of adulthood. But even so, they were aware that the grown ups of their world considered it a matter shrouded in dirtiness and shame. And because children have forever been able, they instinctively knew how to use it to hurt Heath. Heath, however, due to her upbringing, knew a great deal about poverty and desperation; she understood what prostitution was, and because she was also imaginative and caring, images of her sweet and loving Jenny being forced to earn money on the street rose unbidden in her mind's eye so that her heart cramped and burned within her chest. Heath was also rather more used to solving conflicts with her fists than her new school mates were.

Ironically, it could have easily gone in entirely the other direction. —Through the natural force of her nature, Heath could have won any number of admirers and lasting friends from the children as easily as catching snowflakes. With enough time even the teacher, a bitter and snobbish woman, could have been hers. Heath held such power. But at this time in her life she was not yet aware of it; at present, her power was a simple extension of her heart, and it flung about like a willow switch as her soul twisted. Indeed, her loneliness and heaviness of spirit expressed themselves in ways which immediately affected those around her, begging that they prove her right; that she was correct to dread coming to this place. To school.

Before being rediscovered and going to live with her aunt and uncle Jay at the age of nine, Heath had seen the insides of three cold and crowded orphanages, (each one colder and more crowded than the last), and during those years she had learned what it meant to be hungry and poor. At the age of seven, however, her situation improved greatly and for two years she found herself living in the serving hall of a large townhouse in a city in the east. Every Sunday in that townhouse the lord of the manor, old and unusual in his ways, would come downstairs and speak solemnly to the serving staff about such things like where you went when you died, and about behaving correctly and so forth. And once, the old lord had taken Heath and two of the other young girls from the serving staff on a carriage ride. He took his carriage into a dirty, un-cared for part of town and he pointed to some women at the street side. The women were dressed in bright red silks and lacy clothes unlike the other woman Heath was familiar with, and they returned his looks with belligerence and toughened spirit and with coos and laughs. The old lord pursed his lips and spoke in his solemn tone, referring to them as 'fallen women', and the serving girls nodded silently with round eyes and a fearful, half-understanding in their hearts.

Heath knew what prostitution was, and while she had difficulty despising those woman as her old lord and the other serving girls did, the mere thought of her sweet and loving aunt Jenny being forced to earn money on the streets struck such a chord that her heart fairly cramped and died inside her with anguish and fear. She very nearly *did* knock the boy's teeth from his head; lucky for everybody, she gave him a black-eye instead! —The teacher owed Jenny a debt, but not one so great that she would allow a wild-child among her class of carefully bred children! (Jenny spoke with the teacher, a Mrs. Pickle, and Heath was given a second chance. Mrs. Pickle gave in but turned up her nose so high that Heath could see right up her nostrils).

The following day, Heath went to school with her stomach tied in a nervous knot and her eyes set hard and sharp so that the other kids would know not to make trouble for her, (they didn't), and Rubel, like a tabby cat, padded invisibly after Jenny Porter to find out where she worked. . .

HM. SHE WORKS AT A CUSTOMS OFFICE.

I KNEW HEATH WAS WRONG!

KOPFMAN & H... CUSTOMS CLEAR... —BY ROYAL DECREE—

I DON'T LIKE THAT SHE HAS TO WORK DOWN HERE, THOUGH... THIS CAN BE A DANGEROUS PLACE...

WELL, AT LEAST THE PRESS GANGS DON'T BOTHER LADIES!

I CAN TELL HEATH THAT KIO AT SCHOOL WAS LYING TO HER.

—SHE'LL SURE BE GLAD ABOUT THAT!

—THEN MAYBE THINGS WILL BE FIXED UP.

HEATH AND VARKIAS ARE REALLY MAD WITH ME FOR KISSING SORACIA...

IT'S MY OWN STUPID FAULT, I GUESS...

I DON'T EVEN KNOW WHY I DID IT.

—EXCEPT THAT IT FELT REALLY GOOD...

HER LIPS WERE SO SOFT. —AND THEY WEREN'T COLD AT ALL. I THOUGHT SHE'D HAVE COLD LIPS.

I JUST WISH SHE WASN'T SO SCARY!

HRM..! MAYBE HEATH AND VARKIAS WILL FORGIVE ME WHEN I GO BACK AND TELL THEM THAT MRS. PORTER ISN'T A PROSTITUTE.

MAYBE THAT WILL FIX THINGS.

SIGH. NOT LIKELY.

I SURE WISH I STILL HAD A BEST FRIEND.

BELIEVE IT.

WE ARE TEMPTING DEATH VERY MUCH IN THIS, I THINK!

BLACK CASPER IS A SHREWD MAN, BUT HIS ANGER MAKES HIM A FOOL SOMETIMES.

I SOMEHOW THOUGHT IT WOULD BE MORE DIFFICULT...

—THE PRINCE HAS HALF HIS ARMY TRYING TO CATCH THIS KID!

HM!

AND *THAT* IS WHY. THEY WILL FAIL.

ONLY A **GIRL** CAN CATCH A THIEF.

AND IT WOULD BE MORE DIFFICULT IF I WANTED HIS SOUL.

BUT FLESH AND BLOOD IS ALL I NEED TO PAY MY DEBT!

LET US BE GONE NOW.

—QUICKLY.

THERE ARE **SHADOWS** IN THIS CITY WHO HAVE **EYES** AND WOULD KILL US WITHOUT A THOUGHT!

THIS THIEF HAS TOO MANY FRIENDS!

RUBEL NEVER SHOWED UP.

MAYBE HE'S WAITING AT THE HOUSE.

MAYBE...

HOW WAS SCHOOL?

HRM.

SO, I HEAR YOU ATTACKED ANOTHER CHILD AT SCHOOL.

YESTERDAY.

YES, I KNOW.

I HEARD ALL ABOUT IT AT MY CARDS PARTY. —EVERYBODY WAS TALKING ABOUT IT! —SAYING WHAT A VICIOUS LITTLE GIRL YOU ARE!

HOW DO YOU THINK I FEEL HAVING TO HEAR ABOUT SUCH THINGS THROUGH GOSSIP? —NEITHER YOU NOR JENNY THOUGHT TO INFORM ME? I WAS MORTIFIED!

MAYBE BECAUSE IT'S NONE OF HER DAMNED BUSINESS!

WHAT POSSESSED YOU TO DO SUCH A THING?

—NOT THAT I AM AT ALL SURPRISED ABOUT SUCH BEHAVIOR FROM YOU.

WELL?

SOME KID SAID JENNY WAS A PIRATE.

...

AND WORSE.

WHAT?

HOW DARE YOU?!

THERE ARE NO PIRATES IN MY FAMILY.

WHO TOLD YOU THAT?!

enny turned as Smith Robins jogged up to her. "I finished my duties early," he explained brightly. "I thought I'd drop by and see how you were doing."

"Oh, well!" she gave him a warm smile. "I'm doing quite well, thank you."

"And your niece?"

"Oh, Heath. She's settling in. —Though, she had a bit of trouble at school yesterday. It was her first day. . ."

A flicker of distaste crossed Smith Robin's expression and the young guardsman made a thoughtful sound.

"What is it?"

He grumbled. "Oh. . . Nothing. Nothing." He thought some more. "You chose *that* school. . ."

"Yes. . ?"

"Hrm." He frowned and went silent. The two didn't look at one another for a moment.

"Well, I know that Zelga is a fine woman," Jenny said, shifting her hips. "Forthright and sensible. It's good to be around people like that. But Heath is just a girl and working and scrimping for a living is no way to grow up! I know other children sometimes have to work, but I don't think it's right. And she's so *serious*. It's not healthy in someone so young."

"I suppose not. . ."

"She's clearly the sort of girl who's meant for an education," Jenny said firmly. "Even if I can only get her into that school two days a week. It's better than nothing."

Smith Robins frowned at his boots. "Hrm," he said again.

"What? She's quite brilliant."

"I just don't like those *attitudes*. The aristocracy-" Smith Robins began before checking himself. He was a young man and he had a number of the strong opinions young men sometimes have. But he had also grown old enough to know that strong opinions spoken too vehemently could make enemies, especially with people like Jenny who he didn't yet know very well but who he wanted very much to like him. He weighed his words carefully. "All the kids in that school are from very rich families. I don't even know how you managed to get her *into* a school like that." He looked up at her. "How did you?"

Jenny eyed him a moment. "My husband was quite well known. There are some favours still owing. . ."

Smith Robins' expression flickered something for a moment. "The

"thing is. . ," he said, making up his mind and setting his feet firmly apart upon the paving stones, "they *want* the poor to stay poor. And they do everything in their power to ensure it! There's nothing they won't do! They *really* think they're different inside; that their spirits are stronger and better, and they believe if they're not careful, their precious stock will become diluted. There really isn't anything they won't do! I've seen it. I've *lived* with it, Jenny! I think you're making a mistake sending her among them. They'll hurt her or they'll corrupt her. I *know*. . !"

Jenny sighed. She recognized this kind of thinking. These were the kinds of thoughts which could fill one with obsession and bitterness. They could run in endless circles in a person's mind without ever finding solution. "Oh, Smith Robins. . . I suppose you must speak so fiercely."

"I think it's important," he said, but looked a little sheepish for his outburst.

Jenny laughed and turned her head skyward. "Yes. I know. My mother. . . It's the most important thing in her life. I think she is bitter simply because she knows that no matter how hard she pretends or wishes, she will never be anything more than what she is. And we aren't *that* poor. There are many worse off. But she'll never see it that way. So I put up

with it. And I'll certainly put up with it all if it means Heath will be able to read and write! You won't find any good schools for the poor."

"Yes! That's another thing. . !" Smith Robins growled, his stance fierce again. "Why should learning be restricted so!"

Jenny laughed, but not unkindly, and the young man stopped again and let out his breath in a long puff, deflating. "I'm sorry," he said, his sheepish expression becoming more so. "I must watch myself. We soldier-monkeys aren't allowed to have opinions, you know. But you do *understand?*"

"Yes. Yes, I do. But it is not always so black and white. And there are always ways to be found." She paused. "And you're hardly a monkey!"

"Heh. No, but you know how the military is. Orders without questions. If you do ask a question, they take it as a challenge to their authority, and they won't have that. Their self-importance is easily bruised by any long look; by anything but immediate obedience! There are many small men in the prince's army."

"Ha ha! I see. Well, yes, you certainly shan't last long with those attitudes, Smith Robins." Jenny shook her head and smiled warmly again at the young man. He was a picture of ferocity, but somehow seemed leashed by his own desire to behave acceptably. The result gave him an air of farcical confusion. He looked at her and smiled apologetically and she laughed again. "Oh, Smith Robins."

"I know. I know," he said, shaking his head. "But I've been learning things recently. More than I thought I ever would. Two friends of mine came back last evening from naval duty in the South. From Gantry."

"Where they were fighting king Amistus?"

"Hmp!" Smith Robins scowled. "Bloody empire building! I was a fool to join the army. *This* army!"

Jenny squinted at him with guarded fascination.

"If they cannot run their own kingdom without savagery," she asked cautiously, "then why not us? We can bring civility to their shores. —That's what everybody is saying."

"Is that what you believe?" He looked at her directly.

She paused.

"I hardly know what to believe. Why? Do you know something? Is it a military secret?"

"Absolutely! Pain of death. But I wasn't there, so I wasn't given the orders to silence. I'll tell you that the battle for Gantry was nothing short of a massacre! Bloody and unfair. The only resistance were a few farmers with hoes and rakes. Just men trying to protect their families. The truth of it is their whole standing militia pulled out and *let* us in! That's black deal-making, for certain! And our forces. . ." His faced turned dark. "Well, we are the best armed nation in the known world. And we took no prisoners. Women, children. Livestock. Everything was cut down. The countryside was wretched with blood, and then we burned it all. All of Gantry was in flames and now there's nothing left."

Jenny's eyes opened wide and she took a step back. "Are you sure? That's horrible! Even the children? But why? Why would we do that. . ?"

"And old people. Our troops have been brutal before, but it's all just been showing muscle. This was different; the prince wanted the whole of Gantry wiped off the map, and he did it. There's nothing left. And he's only just starting. I've heard rumours of *real* battles being planned. I don't know if you know, but ambassadors have been leaving Highborn. They've been leaving, or they've been *disappearing*."

"You can't be serious!" Jenny felt her chest tighten and her heart begin to race. She steadied herself on the bannister.

"I am. And all these troops here in our own streets. . ." Smith Robins leaned close and spoke low. "A lot of people think it's a *good* thing! I've had to put my hand into matters more than once to keep heads from inflaming. I've even heard stories about civilians being murdered by the Prince Guard! And from what I've seen, I can believe it! I tell you, Jenny, It's more than just

WHAT A STRANGE FELLOW!

I WONDER IF HE WAS ONE OF THOSE MAD BOG-HERMITS MOTHER TALKS ABOUT...

AND A TAME FOX FOR A PET!

HOLD ON... —THERE *IS* A MESSAGE IN HERE!

IT WAS JUST STUCK TO THE INSIDE OF THE TUBE...

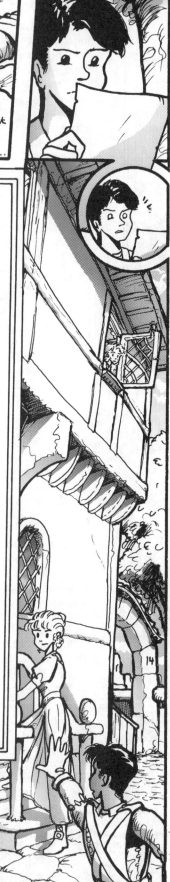

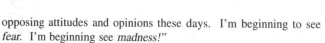

opposing attitudes and opinions these days. I'm beginning to see *fear*. I'm beginning see *madness!*"

Jenny nodded tightly and replied, lowering her voice. "I don't think you are imagining things," she said. "And I feel safe in telling you that there are other things going on as well. Far stranger things!"

Smith Robins squinted at her, his face a mask of intensity. "Are you talking about *magic?*" he whispered. A shiver shot up and down his spine. *Both* their spines.

Jenny looked around, glancing at the road and the windows of the other houses. "Oh, I really can't say anything more! Not here. My mother is waiting inside for me."

As if on cue, Vale's voice raised from inside the house, impatient, calling to her daughter.

"I know, I have to go anyway." Smith Robins said quickly. "Or they'll get suspicious."

Suspicious. He used the word without a thought and neither of them noticed. It had swept them both up *that* quickly. They were alight now, like a pair of wild deer alert in a dark wood. But the sun was warm and the breeze was fragrant and birds chirped from the cool green of the poplar beside Jenny's house. Heath strained to listen to their words, the hairs all prickled up on her neck. She had felt like this before. It had been like this in Millbrook in the days just before Quinton was arrested.

"Perhaps we should talk later," Smith Robins suggested, breaking the spell.

"Yes! We must!"

"Tomorrow. I can meet you after work. I could walk you home."

"Yes. Yes. I'll be waiting!" Without thinking, Jenny put her hand to his forearm and grasped him firmly. The effect of the touch was surprising to them both, interrupting their thoughts. With that, they were both alight with something *else*. A flickering feeling both bright and exciting. Jenny removed her hand.

"I'll see you tomorrow!" Smith Robins whispered, holding her eyes with his own the way young men of intensity will sometimes do. Then, with both their hearts filled with giddiness and danger, he turned and dashed away.

Chapter 3

SHH..! HE'S WAKING UP.

HE'S CUTE!

GROAN...

WHERE AM I?

WE'RE POWERFUL ENCHANTRESSES.

WE RESCUED YOU FROM BLACK CASPER, THE PIRATE. HE WAS GOING TO KILL YOU.

I'M STILL TIED UP.

THAT'S BECAUSE YOU'RE OUR PRISONER NOW.

LOCUMIRE DIDN'T WANT US TO KILL BLACK CASPER AND HIS PIRATES, SO WE BOUGHT YOU FROM THEM INSTEAD.

LOCUMIRE, THE WITCH QUEEN!

OOOH. I FEEL WOOZY.

DON'T WORRY. —SHE ONLY WANTS TO TORTURE YOU, AND THEN SHE'LL LET YOU GO.

YOU'LL PROBABLY STILL BE ABLE TO EAT SOFT FOODS.

ARE YOU INSANE?! TELLING ME THAT DOESN'T MAKE ME FEEL ANY BETTER AT ALL!

ACTUALLY, LOCUMIRE SAID SHE WAS GOING TO KILL HIM WHEN IT'S OVER.

REALLY? OH NO!

I'M SORRY. I DIDN'T MEAN TO GET YOUR HOPES UP.

LOCUMIRE ONLY WANTS TO HURT YOU BECAUSE SHE'S MAD AT SORACIA. SHE KNOWS SORACIA LOVES YOU.

HM. —GOOD THING I'M NOT GOING TO BE TORTURED FOR ANYTHING I DID.

I'M VERY PLEASED.

YOU'RE BEING SARCASTIC!

HE HAS TO BE. SARCASM IS A GOOD WAY TO DEAL WITH FEELING FUTILE.

OH.. YOU DON'T HAVE TO FEEL FUTILE.

YOU'RE REALLY COOL! WHY ELSE WOULD SORACIA TELL US SHE LOVED YOU?

ACTUALLY, KNOWING HER...

I'M GOING TO LET YOU GO!

WOW. THANKS!

YOU PROMISE TO VISIT ME BY MOONLIGHT AND KEEP ME IN YOUR FONDEST THOUGHTS?

SURE, AS LONG AS SORACIA AND PRINCESS KATARA DON'T MIND.

WHY SHOULD IT MATTER WHAT THEY THINK?

UM...

I'M BACK WITH INSTRUCTIONS!

LOCUMIRE WANTS THE THIEF TAKEN UP TO THE PALACE—PETTY!

WE'RE GOING TO PUT YOU IN A COFFIN AND LOCK IT SHUT!

A COFFIN?

WILL YOU BE SCARED?

NO! I'M GOING TO MAKE LOTS OF NOISE SO PEOPLE STOP YOU AND LET ME OUT!

GEE. CLEVER.

—LOCUMIRE ALSO SAID TO LET YOU HAVE SOME WATER BEFORE WE GO.

YOU'RE GOING TO DRUG ME?!

I'M NOT DRINKING THAT! —YOU PUT SLEEP DRUG IN IT!

GEE, YOU'RE SMART.

AND YOU KNOW WHAT? —LOCUMIRE SAID IF YOU FIGURED OUT IT WASN'T JUST WATER, WE COULD TORTURE YOU UNTIL YOU DRANK IT!

YOU LET HIM FIND OUT ON PURPOSE!

HA! —I'LL USE PASSIVE RESISTANCE! —I'LL LET YOU HURT ME UNTIL YOU FEEL SO ASHAMED OF YOURSELF THAT YOU CAN'T HELP BUT STOP!

THAT DOESN'T SOUND LIKE IT WILL WORK AT ALL.

ACTUALLY, IT MADE MORE SENSE WHEN QUINTON DESCRIBED IT TO ME...

THERE ARE TEN-THOUSAND YEARS OF CONSTRUCTS DOWN HERE! ALL CRIS-CROSSING. AND SHIFTING ABOUT, TOO, I'M ALMOST CERTAIN.

SHIFTING ABOUT?

HIGHBORN IS BUILT UPON AN OLD WOUND IN THE EARTH. THIS IS WHERE THE **LOST LEGIONS** CAME THROUGH.

WHO?

I TOLD YOU ABOUT THEM ONCE.

FROM ONE OF YOUR DREAMS WHEN WE LIVED UNDER THE BRIDGE?

I MUST HAVE BEEN DOZING.

ALL THOSE STORIES RAN TOGETHER AFTER A WHILE.

I'LL TELL IT TO YOU AGAIN SOMEDAY. —I KNOW IT BETTER NOW.

TWO WORLDS TOUCH SOMEWHERE BENEATH ALL OF THIS. WORLD MAGIC LEAKS THROUGH THESE STONES. —BENEATH ALL OF OCEANSEND.

BENEATH THE MOUNTAIN ESPECIALLY.

HRM.

PERHAPS IT IS NOT A GOOD IDEA TO BRING TROOPS THROUGH HERE AFTER ALL...

NO. IT'S BEEN DONE BEFORE. WE'LL NEED SCOUTS AND SUCH, BUT WE CAN DO IT. —IT'LL TAKE TIME TO MAP THE AREA; TO MAKE IT OUR OWN.

I'LL NEED TO FIGURE OUT HOW THE PATTERNS AND INFLUENCES MOVE DOWN HERE.

—AT ONE TIME YOU COULD GET LOST IN THE MOST PECULIAR WAYS.

YOU COULD GO EXPLORING AS WE ARE NOW, AND COME UP AGAIN IN A DIFFERENT PLACE ENTIRELY.

—IN A DIFFERENT **WORLD**, IN DIFFERENT **TIMES**, EVEN!

BUT I THINK IT'S SETTLED SOMEWHAT SINCE THOSE DAYS.

I CERTAINLY HOPE SO!

COME ON, GRINDLE. YOU'RE NOT USED TO BIG, OPEN PLACES, BUT IT'S OKAY.

WHERE ARE WE?

SOMEWHERE SAFE.

YAWN

IT'S THE PRINCESS!

THE PRINCESS IS BACK!

YAY!

BASE CAMP

HOORAY!

SIT DOWN, GRINDLE. —I WANT TO TAKE CARE OF THOSE HANDS RIGHT AWAY.

LEADAKE, WOULD YOU FETCH MY MENDING THINGS, PLEASE.

I BROUGHT YOUR WOODS BOOTS, PRINCESS!

SHE'S SEWING HIS HANDS BACK ON..!

OOOCH!

GO ON! YOU DON'T ALL NEED TO WATCH!

DO I HAVE TO CHASE YOU? FINE!

ZZZZZ

ZZZZZ CHASE? WHAZZUT?!

>BLINK<

I'M UP!

I'M UP!

YAWN

>STRETCH<

>SMACK SMACK!<

SAY HELLO TO QUINTON, GRINDLE.

HE'S OUR PRISONER.

HI.

UM..., HELLO.

NEW RECRUIT?

I FOUND HIM UNDER THE CITY WITH HIS HANDS CUT OFF.

—IT WAS SALLY.

SHE'S STILL CRUEL AND SELFISH.

HM! AND HOW EXACTLY DO YOU PLAN TO CONDUCT YOUR-SELF ONCE YOU'VE FINISHED RAISING YOUR ARMY?

I'LL BE A TERROR AND PEOPLE WILL FEAR AND DESPISE ME, I'M SURE.

BAH! NOTHING YOU DO MAKES ANY SENSE! —IT'S HAVING TWO OF YOU ABOUT THAT'S DRIVEN YOU MAD!

I ONLY HOPE HEATH HASN'T LOST HER NOODLES AS WELL!

THERE! ALL DONE!

YOU KNOW... OF ALL THE THINGS I'VE SEEN, THERE IS ONLY ONE WHICH I DON'T FULLY UNDERSTAND.

THERE'S MORE THAN ONE THING, KIDDO.

YES, BUT THIS QUESTION YOU CAN ANSWER.

WHY LOCUMIRE? I DON'T UNDERSTAND WHY YOUR BROTHER CHOSE HER.

SHE IS DANGEROUS, TO BE CERTAIN, BUT... HOW DO I DESCRIBE IT...

SHE DOES NOT HAVE THAT ELUSIVE QUALITY TO WHICH PEOPLE ARE DRAWN. —FROM ALL THE STRONG AND ANGRY GIRLS WHO FIRST HEARD HIS WHISPER, THERE MUST HAVE BEEN A DOZEN CRAFTIER, AND MORE DETERMINED THAN HER! —THAT IS WHY HE HAS HER BREEDING GIRLS FILLED WITH SUCH FIRE AND VANITY. —TO MAKE UP FOR ALL HER DEFICIENCIES.

AND IT IS A CLEVER PLAN, EXCEPT IT IS NOT YOUR BROTHER'S. —HE SO FEARS THE THOUGHT OF HIS STATURE BEING REDUCED BY THE ANXIOUS. —HE MUCH PREFERS SERVANTS LIKE MY BROTHER THE PRINCE; COOL AND ARROGANT AND CAPABLE.

THAT'S HOW WE'VE ALWAYS BEATEN HIM IN THE PAST. —THE SELF LOVING AND ARROGANT ALWAYS OVER-STEP THEMSELVES.

HIS USING LOCUMIRE BOTHERS ME AND I WANT TO KNOW WHY IT HAPPENED.

—BUT FIRST, ANOTHER QUESTION: WHY DOES SHE STILL PLAGUE YOU?

SHE TRAPPED YOU UNDER THAT TREE! HOW COULD SHE? IT SEEMS IMPOSSIBLE TO ME THAT YOU COULD NOT STAMP HER OUT IN LESS THAN A MONTH, EVEN WITH ALL THIS NEW POWER SHE HAS GAINED.

IS IT THIS APPARENTLY UNCONQUERABLE QUALITY OF HERS THAT HE KEEPS HER FOR?

I MET HER WHEN SHE WAS VERY YOUNG.

SHE WAS JUST A LITTLE GIRL; THE DAUGHTER OF A FRIEND OF MINE.

LORD LOCUMIRE.

I WAS LOOKING FOR YOU...

OH MY!

YOU THOUGHT SHE WAS ME!

BUT I'M NOTHING LIKE HER!

YOU CAN SENSE ME FROM HALF-WAY ACROSS THE WORLD!

SHE HAD YOUR EYES.

IT WAS AN UNDERHANDED TRICK.

THE FORCES OF DARKNESS WON A BATTLE THAT DAY!

IT WAS A MISTAKE.

HOW DID I KNOW ANYTHING BEYOND MY SHABBY LITTLE WORLD EACH TIME?

YOU!

EVERYTHING WAS YOU, QUINTON!

—SO I WANTED MY OWN MEMORIES BACK!

I REMEMBER SITTING CROSS-LEGGED ON THE FLOOR, STARING UP AT YOU.

I REMEMBER...

WATCHING YOU AS IF YOU WERE THE MOST WONDERFUL THING THAT EVER MARCHED ACROSS THE WORLD, CREATING DUST CLOUDS OF THE SETTLED LIVES YOU ADDLED WITH YOUR TEN THOUSAND YEARS!

I THINK ONLY YOUR BROTHER MUST BE MORE WONDERFUL THAN YOU, —ALL DARK AND DRAMATIC, I EXPECT.

OH, AND WHEN I MEET YOUR BROTHER, I SHALL BLOW KISSES TO HIM, AND DRIVE HIM QUITE MAD.

I BREATHED ALMOST NOT AT ALL, FEELING YOUR SUN ON MY FACE WHILE YOU TOLD YOUR STORIES TO ME. "OH," I THOUGHT, "HOW MANY LIVES HAVE I LIVED BEFORE? HOW MANY DREAMS HAVE I HAD BEFORE NOW?"

"HOW MANY SEAS AND DESERTS HAVE I PLIED? WHAT ADVENTURES HAVE I KNOWN?"

I CRIED FOR MY LOST MEMORIES.

—I CRIED FOR ALL MY FRIENDS I NEVER KNEW!

I'VE NEVER HURT LIKE THAT BEFORE.

Chapter 4

I DIED BEFORE YOU BROUGHT THEM TO LIFE.

AND BY THE TIME I'D WOKEN AGAIN, YOU'D CAUSED DISASTER WITH THEM AND SENT THEM OFF TO BE LOST AND NEVER FOUND AGAIN.

FIFTEEN YEARS BETWEEN.

I REALLY DON'T LIKE THOSE GAPS IN MY MEMORY!

WELL THEY WERE EASY ENOUGH TO FIND.

I KNOW ALL YOUR HIDING PLACES.

THAT'S BECAUSE I USED TO TRUST YOU!

I USED TO BE TRUSTWORTHY.

PROBLEM IS I'VE USED EVERY BIT OF KNOWLEDGE I HAVE UPON THEM;

EVERY SCRAP OF MAGIC.

BUT I CAN'T GET THEM WORKING AT ALL; WHICH ISN'T SURPRISING, I SUPPOSE.

WHATEVER IT WAS THAT GAVE THEM LIFE RESIDES IN YOUR SKULL ALONE.

HA! AND IT'S NOT EVEN IN MY SKULL ANYMORE.

I FORGOT IT!

OH, I'M SURE YOU CAN TELL ME IF YOU THINK HARD.

NEVER! THE FOLLY OF MY ERRORS WILL NOT TERRORIZE THE WORLD AGAIN!

THESE THINGS CAN'T BE CONTROLLED! THEY'RE AN ABOMINATION OF ENGINEERING! —THE DREGS OF MY SHODDIEST THINKING!

THE IRON GUARD ARE AT LEAST DRIVEN BY LOST SOULS! BUT THESE...

THESE ARE SPRINGS AND MAGIC COMBINED; THEY WILL NEVER RUN DOWN!

BAH! I'LL NEVER SLEEP!

YOUR SOLDIERS MAY HAVE FED ME A HUGE, WARM PASTA LUNCHEON, BUT I'LL NOT DROWSE FOR YOU!

YOUR MAD TREACHERY WILL BE OF NO AVAIL!

YAWN

HRM!

YOU'RE MISTAKEN IF YOU THINK YOU'VE WON!

I NEED ONLY CONCENTRATE ON STAYING AWAKE!

—MY INTRENCHED POWERS OF SELF-DISCIPLINE WILL MAKE RAGS OF ALL YOUR DEVIOUS PLANS!

OF COURSE, LYING DOWN AND RESTING MY EYES CAN ONLY HELP TO REDUCE THE RISK OF MY BECOMING EXHAUSTED...

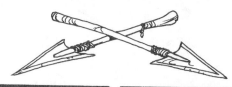

I KNEW YOU WERE GOING TO ESCAPE. —IT WAS INEVITABLE, BUT YOU DIDN'T HAVE TO BE SO MEAN ABOUT IT!

YOU SHOULD BE ASHAMED!

MEAN?

ASHAMED?!

ASHAMED OF TRYING TO ESCAPE YOUR MAD CLUTCHES AND WARN THE WORLD OF YOUR DESPERATE SCHEMES?!

NEVER!!

HOLD YOUR GROUND!

HM.

TIE HIM UP AND TAKE HIM BACK TO HIS PRISON.

AND TAKE CARE TO IGNORE ALL HE SAYS!

WORDS AND HONESTY ARE HIS SPELLS AND TRICKERY. —ALL ROADS LEAD TO AND FROM KALUVINAR IF YOU LEND HIM YOUR HEART BUT ONCE!

OUR ROAD TREADS A PATH BEYOND HIS COMPREHENSION; OURS IS THE GREATER GOOD AND TRUE SIGHT IS OUR GREATEST ALLY!

LE'S GET MOVING!

YOU HEARD HER, TROLLS; WE'VE GOT OUR OWN ROAD!

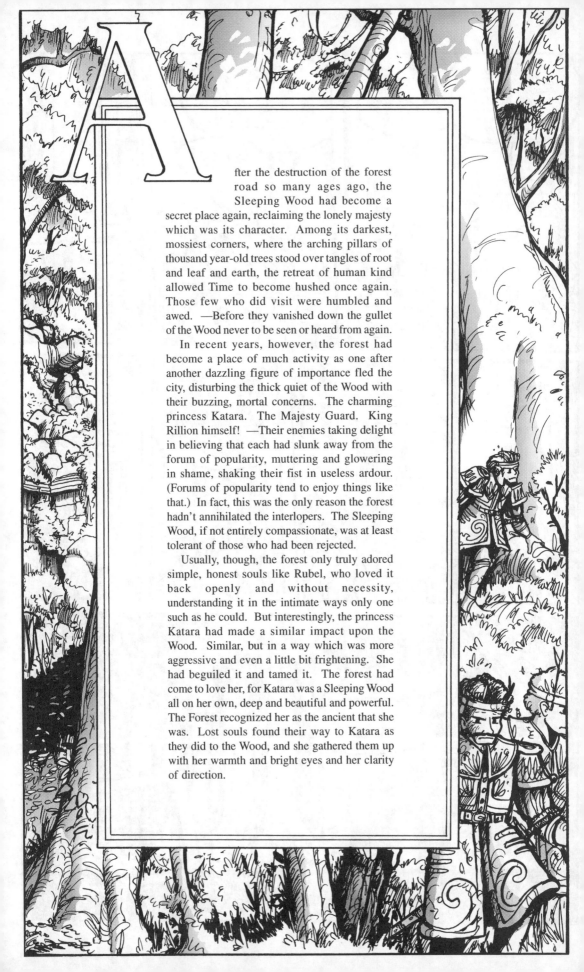

A fter the destruction of the forest road so many ages ago, the Sleeping Wood had become a secret place again, reclaiming the lonely majesty which was its character. Among its darkest, mossiest corners, where the arching pillars of thousand year-old trees stood over tangles of root and leaf and earth, the retreat of human kind allowed Time to become hushed once again. Those few who did visit were humbled and awed. —Before they vanished down the gullet of the Wood never to be seen or heard from again.

In recent years, however, the forest had become a place of much activity as one after another dazzling figure of importance fled the city, disturbing the thick quiet of the Wood with their buzzing, mortal concerns. The charming princess Katara. The Majesty Guard. King Rillion himself! —Their enemies taking delight in believing that each had slunk away from the forum of popularity, muttering and glowering in shame, shaking their fist in useless ardour. (Forums of popularity tend to enjoy things like that.) In fact, this was the only reason the forest hadn't annihilated the interlopers. The Sleeping Wood, if not entirely compassionate, was at least tolerant of those who had been rejected.

Usually, though, the forest only truly adored simple, honest souls like Rubel, who loved it back openly and without necessity, understanding it in the intimate ways only one such as he could. But interestingly, the princess Katara had made a similar impact upon the Wood. Similar, but in a way which was more aggressive and even a little bit frightening. She had beguiled it and tamed it. The forest had come to love her, for Katara was a Sleeping Wood all on her own, deep and beautiful and powerful. The Forest recognized her as the ancient that she was. Lost souls found their way to Katara as they did to the Wood, and she gathered them up with her warmth and bright eyes and her clarity of direction.

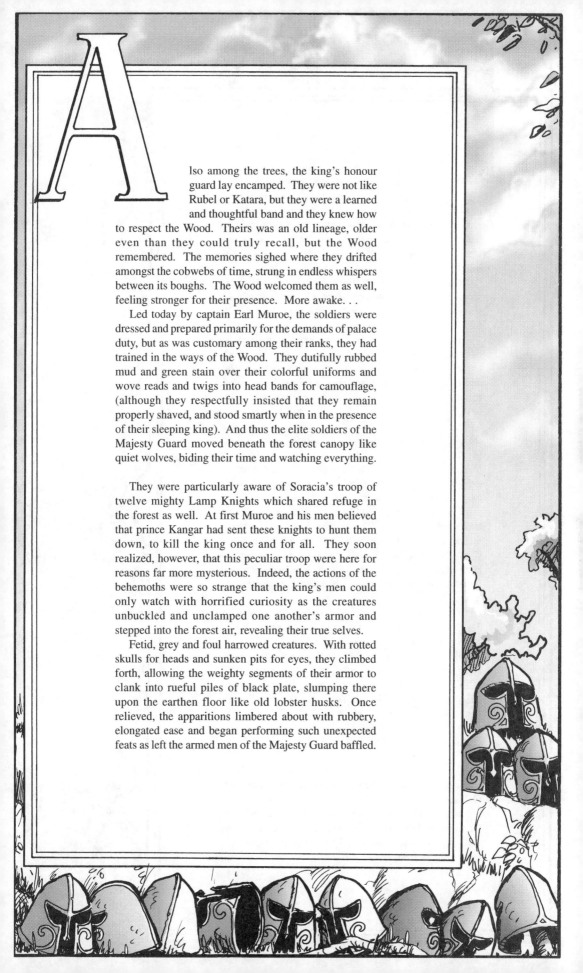

lso among the trees, the king's honour guard lay encamped. They were not like Rubel or Katara, but they were a learned and thoughtful band and they knew how to respect the Wood. Theirs was an old lineage, older even than they could truly recall, but the Wood remembered. The memories sighed where they drifted amongst the cobwebs of time, strung in endless whispers between its boughs. The Wood welcomed them as well, feeling stronger for their presence. More awake. . .

Led today by captain Earl Muroe, the soldiers were dressed and prepared primarily for the demands of palace duty, but as was customary among their ranks, they had trained in the ways of the Wood. They dutifully rubbed mud and green stain over their colorful uniforms and wove reads and twigs into head bands for camouflage, (although they respectfully insisted that they remain properly shaved, and stood smartly when in the presence of their sleeping king). And thus the elite soldiers of the Majesty Guard moved beneath the forest canopy like quiet wolves, biding their time and watching everything.

They were particularly aware of Soracia's troop of twelve mighty Lamp Knights which shared refuge in the forest as well. At first Muroe and his men believed that prince Kangar had sent these knights to hunt them down, to kill the king once and for all. They soon realized, however, that this peculiar troop were here for reasons far more mysterious. Indeed, the actions of the behemoths were so strange that the king's men could only watch with horrified curiosity as the creatures unbuckled and unclamped one another's armor and stepped into the forest air, revealing their true selves.

Fetid, grey and foul harrowed creatures. With rotted skulls for heads and sunken pits for eyes, they climbed forth, allowing the weighty segments of their armor to clank into rueful piles of black plate, slumping there upon the earthen floor like old lobster husks. Once relieved, the apparitions limbered about with rubbery, elongated ease and began performing such unexpected feats as left the armed men of the Majesty Guard baffled.

he strange apparitions carefully picked about, choosing and discarding stones which they then pulverized into fine powders. This, mixed with clays, they used to polish their blackened armor. They crushed leaves and flowers and roots so that saps collected and mixed into bright, surprising color, which the creatures used with studied proficiency to inscribe roses of lavish blue upon their capes.

"Ought we to strike them now while they are vulnerable?" asked Muroe's second in command. "We will certainly never get another opportunity so ripe as this!"

The men looked to their captain through their stalks of grass and mud smeared faces, eyes inquiring, ready to move without hesitation. Muroe paused and squinted, and then made a small movement of his head which meant, 'No.' His men all silently turned their gazes back to the scene before them.

The undead horrors moved in a peculiar, understated manner about their tasks; in a fashion which eluded Muroe's thoughts for a long moment, keeping him mesmerized. One zombie sat cross legged while it dabbed at a cloak with a brush made from a shredded twig. It dabbed blue dye, forming the outline of a rose, made an error and stopped to dab now with oil and dry leaf to lift the mistake. The beast sat like a patient tailor, utterly absorbed in the task. All the creatures were similarly focused and thorough in their chores, seeming even graceful for what they were, and yet each was imbued with a muted sadness which filled the atmosphere of the ravine.

"They move as we do," Muroe breathed, blinking. "—As we *would* were we bonded to service for an eternity beyond our lives."

"*Who* do they belong to?" his lieutenant asked in an awed whisper. "These cannot be the prince's beasts!"

"I don't know. —Certainly not! Not the prince. No, it is a mystery," Muroe decided. "We must watch them further."

"Aye."

And that is how that went.

Katara, of course, did not need to watch the knights of Soracia's honor guard in order to understand them. She already knew what they stood for, and she felt pity for them; indeed, they were one of the reasons Katara still loved her sister and would not harm her or drive her loyal knights from the Wood.

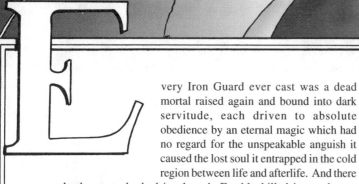

Every Iron Guard ever cast was a dead mortal raised again and bound into dark servitude, each driven to absolute obedience by an eternal magic which had no regard for the unspeakable anguish it caused the lost soul it entrapped in the cold region between life and afterlife. And there were dead men to be had in plenty! Freshly killed in combat or murdered in prison, by blade or disease or both. Strong warriors who had died in health were preferred, simply for their larger frames and greater strength, but in the end even the body of an old man who had died in sickness would rise again with massive, inhuman power. —More than enough to don the black armor and join the horror ranks of the army belonging to an old and now forgotten king who, like prince Kangar, had sold his soul to a minister of the Furious Lord in return for power. —In this case, an invincible army.

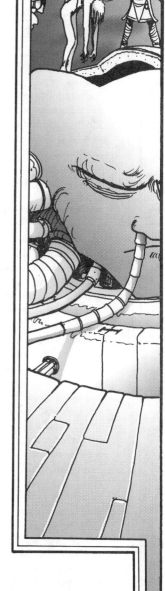

The suffering creatures moaned in a despair without understanding. Their souls, after having disintegrated at death into the component fibres of emotion and thought, even after being strewn once again into the timeless winds of the unknown, were called back, *wrenched* back. Even if by that time they had gathered again into new lives, they were pulled back nonetheless, so powerful and unforgiving was the hand of that magic. And so the precious vitality of new men and new women was thus robbed; their effervescence drained so that eyes dimmed and hearts stopped. It was a disease none understood and for which there was no cure, and all of it so that foul effigies of spent lives could be summoned back.

Worse, the creatures were not reconstructed the way they had been originally; being irreparably damaged and torn in obscene ways by the process. —Through both supernatural and mechanical means, the tiniest fragments of their spirits had been split into pieces *much* smaller than they ever should have gone. In doing this, massive power was made free, granting their undead forms terrible strength. By this same action, Choice and Thought were also divided, crushed into hopelessly small fragments so that the beasts were rendered in their own minds forever lost in a never-ending nightmare of servitude, able now only to comprehend the orders and instructions of those who had recast them. Such were the Lamp Knights of the Iron Guard.

When Soracia was still a young woman, only newly turned to the shadow arts, the Lamp Knights were nothing more than a foul glimmer in the imagination of the Furious Lord. Ramanious was also younger in those days, and hot with such passions and guile as left little room for love. So even as Soracia, beautiful and bold in all the ways which would later make her his *only* passion, even as she entered into his web, he thought little of her. He saw simply that he could use her, and this is exactly what he did.

Thus, as with all disciples of evil, there came a time when Soracia wished for power above all else, and in seeking it, she made a bargain. . .

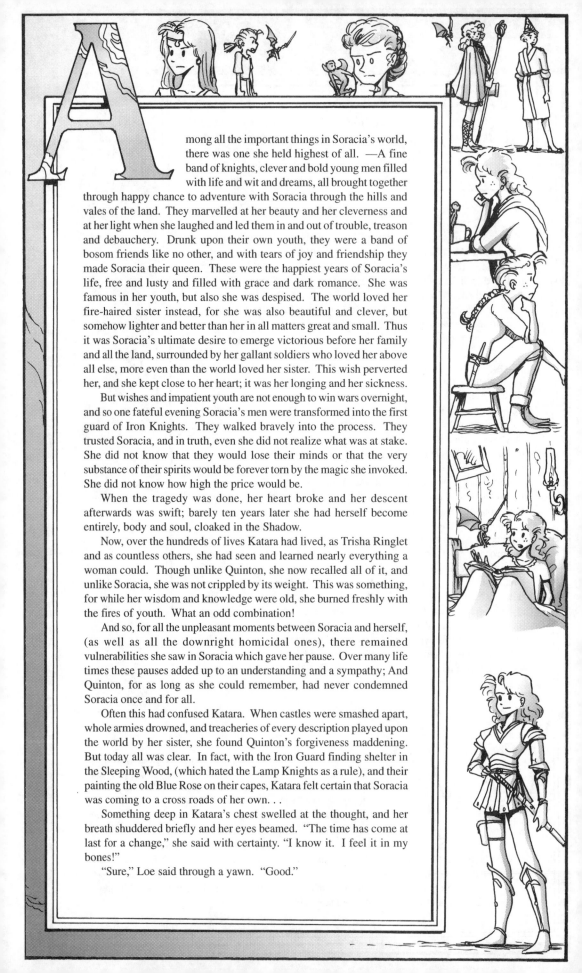

Among all the important things in Soracia's world, there was one she held highest of all. —A fine band of knights, clever and bold young men filled with life and wit and dreams, all brought together through happy chance to adventure with Soracia through the hills and vales of the land. They marvelled at her beauty and her cleverness and at her light when she laughed and led them in and out of trouble, treason and debauchery. Drunk upon their own youth, they were a band of bosom friends like no other, and with tears of joy and friendship they made Soracia their queen. These were the happiest years of Soracia's life, free and lusty and filled with grace and dark romance. She was famous in her youth, but also she was despised. The world loved her fire-haired sister instead, for she was also beautiful and clever, but somehow lighter and better than her in all matters great and small. Thus it was Soracia's ultimate desire to emerge victorious before her family and all the land, surrounded by her gallant soldiers who loved her above all else, more even than the world loved her sister. This wish perverted her, and she kept close to her heart; it was her longing and her sickness.

But wishes and impatient youth are not enough to win wars overnight, and so one fateful evening Soracia's men were transformed into the first guard of Iron Knights. They walked bravely into the process. They trusted Soracia, and in truth, even she did not realize what was at stake. She did not know that they would lose their minds or that the very substance of their spirits would be forever torn by the magic she invoked. She did not know how high the price would be.

When the tragedy was done, her heart broke and her descent afterwards was swift; barely ten years later she had herself become entirely, body and soul, cloaked in the Shadow.

Now, over the hundreds of lives Katara had lived, as Trisha Ringlet and as countless others, she had seen and learned nearly everything a woman could. Though unlike Quinton, she now recalled all of it, and unlike Soracia, she was not crippled by its weight. This was something, for while her wisdom and knowledge were old, she burned freshly with the fires of youth. What an odd combination!

And so, for all the unpleasant moments between Soracia and herself, (as well as all the downright homicidal ones), there remained vulnerabilities she saw in Soracia which gave her pause. Over many life times these pauses added up to an understanding and a sympathy; And Quinton, for as long as she could remember, had never condemned Soracia once and for all.

Often this had confused Katara. When castles were smashed apart, whole armies drowned, and treacheries of every description played upon the world by her sister, she found Quinton's forgiveness maddening. But today all was clear. In fact, with the Iron Guard finding shelter in the Sleeping Wood, (which hated the Lamp Knights as a rule), and their painting the old Blue Rose on their capes, Katara felt certain that Soracia was coming to a cross roads of her own. . .

Something deep in Katara's chest swelled at the thought, and her breath shuddered briefly and her eyes beamed. "The time has come at last for a change," she said with certainty. "I know it. I feel it in my bones!"

"Sure," Loe said through a yawn. "Good."

L oe, the two hundred year-old troll she had first met upon a lonely forest bridge four years earlier, was now her best friend in all the world and the highest ranking officer in her army. The pair lay stretched out on their backs on a warm, flat rock, watching the clouds together while digesting supper. The other trolls made industrious, happy sounds in the camp below.

"Just don't get strange," Loe said after a moment's thought. "I've seen that happen before. —When great leaders start thinking too much of themselves. Don't let it go to your head, or you'll be sorry."

"Hmph. Do you really see that in me?"

"I've seen it before, is all I'm saying. If everything doesn't go your way, you should just be able to know to quit when you're ahead. That's all."

"It's not a gamble, Loe. It can only go the way it is ultimately meant to go. . ," Katara said with finality. "That's all it can ever do."

"You're the sorceress, I guess. I'm just saying, is all." Loe sighed in the summer warmth of the early evening. He rubbed his back against the stone with pleasure. "Pass me another slice of that pie."

"You'll get fat," Katara laughed. "And then we'll be slowed down for real. You'll undo fate all by yourself. —With your belly!" she poked him.

Loe grinned happily. (A rather ugly thing.)

"Pooh," he said.

Chapter 5

MRS. ZELGA, DO YOU THINK IT'S RIGHT THAT JENNY SHOULDN'T BE ALLOWED TO MARRY **SMITH-ROBINS** IF SHE WANTS TO?

THAT'S A VERY SUDDEN QUESTION.

JENNY'S MOTHER SAYS SMITH ROBINS DOESN'T HAVE ANY PROSPECTS OR MONEY, —BUT THAT STINKS! —HE COULD GET A JOB! WHAT'S SO WRONG WITH THAT?

JENNY'S RELATIONSHIP WITH HER MOTHER IS COMPLICATED. —THERE ARE PROBABLY MANY THINGS YOU DON'T KNOW ABOUT THEM.

YEAH. I GET THAT FEELING TOO.

WHY DO YOU THINK JENNY'S MOTHER TREATS HER SO BADLY?

IT'S NOT BECAUSE SHE'S A MEAN OLD LADY?

HEATH, DID YOU GIVE THAT PACKAGE TO JENNY THE OTHER DAY AS I ASKED?

YOU FORGOT?

I'M SORRY! IT WAS AN ACCIDENT! I WAS GOING TO TELL YOU!

I WAS ON THE MOUNTAIN THE DAY THE **LAND-SLIDE** HAPPENED, AND IT FELL. —I NEARLY **DIED**!

UM...

I GUESS THAT MIGHT SOUND A BIT DIFFICULT TO BELIEVE...

WHAT? —THAT YOU WERE GOING TO TELL ME, OR THAT YOU WERE THE CAUSE OF A LANDSLIDE?

IT WASN'T **ALL** MY FAULT!

HM! THAT WAS WEIRD.

WHEN MRS. ZELGA FOUND OUT I LOST THE PACKAGE, SHE DIDN'T GET MAD. —SHE JUST SAID "SHE'D HAVE TO FIND ANOTHER WAY."

THAT'S VERY MYSTERIOUS. —I WONDER WHAT SHE MEANT.

SHE PROBABLY JUST DECIDED NOT TO LET YOU DO DELIVERIES FOR HER.

GEE. I HOPE THAT'S NOT IT. —THAT WOULD MEAN SHE DOESN'T TRUST ME!

WELL, YOU **DID** LOSE THE LAST PACKAGE WHEN YOU TRASHED QUINTON'S TOWER.

ARGH! IT WASN'T MY FAULT!

YES IT WAS. —I WAS THERE.

MEANWHILE...

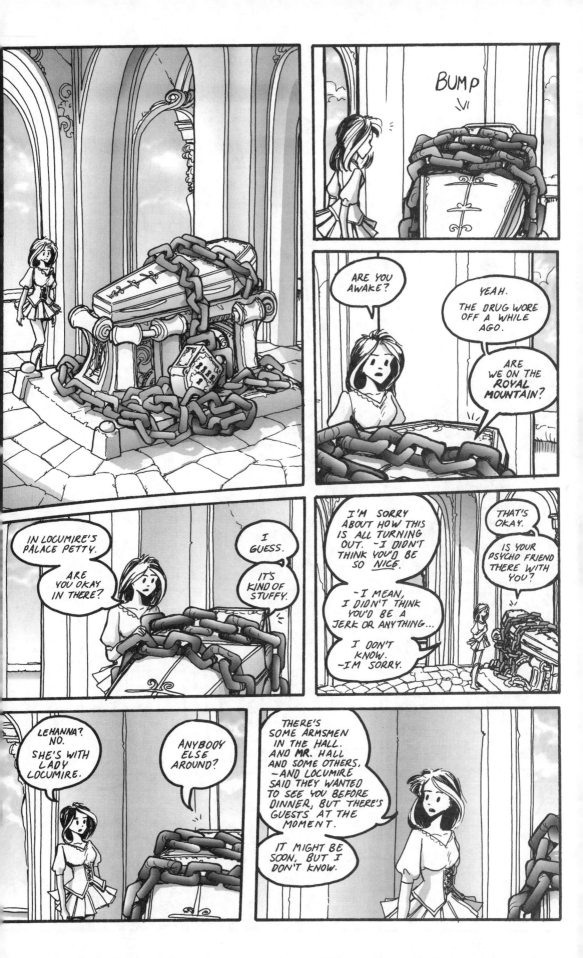

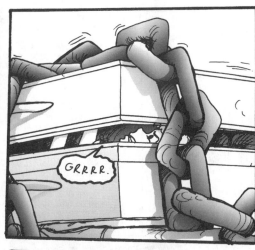

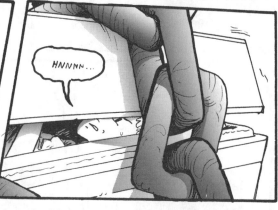

WHOA!

YEAH. THEY CAME UP ON OUR SHIP WHEN IT WAS NIGHT TIME AND FOGGY, AND THEY ATTACKED. —WE WERE CAUGHT COMPLETELY OFF OUR GUARD AND THEY KILLED HALF OUR CREW.

—THEY WOULDN'T HAVE TAKEN US SO EASILY IF MY GRANDFATHER WASN'T LAID UP WITH A BROKEN LEG. —AND IT TOOK FIVE OF THEM TO KNOCK HIM DOWN EVEN THEN!

—THEY TIED US ALL UP ON THE DECK.

—ERK OW!

WHAT'S WRONG?

IT'S HARD TO MOVE IN HERE. —I JUST HAD TO GET MY KNIFE.

HOW COME YOU DIDN'T TAKE IT AWAY FROM ME?

THE ROPES WE TIED YOU UP IN HAD A SPELL SO YOU WOULDN'T BE ABLE TO CUT THEM.

LEAHANNA HOPED YOU'D TRY TO ESCAPE USING YOUR KNIFE. SHE SAID IT WOULD BE DISHEARTENING FOR YOU.

SHE'S REALLY NOT VERY NICE TO BOYS!

WELL I BET SHE'LL GET IN TROUBLE WITH LOCUMIRE!

—GRUNT—

THIS'LL BE WAY EASIER THAN IF I HAD TO USE MY BELT-BUCKLE!

≥CUT≤

RIIPPPP!

WHAT ARE YOU DOING?

CUTTING THE LINING...

KONK

HM.

THIS IS REALLY STRONG WOOD. —I NEED MORE LEVERAGE.

IT'D SURE BE EASIER IF I COULD SEE WHAT I WAS DOING!

ERK MPH..

YANK

ERRRR

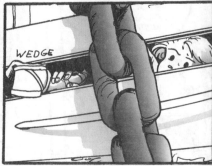

WEDGE

WOW, THAT'S HEAVY! I CAN SEE NOW, THOUGH.

CRUSH

SO WHAT HAPPENED NEXT?

AFTER THE PIRATES TIED EVERYONE UP, IS THAT WHEN THEY PUT YOU IN A BOX AND THREW YOU INTO THE OCEAN?

NO.

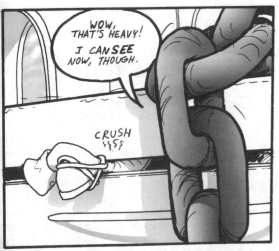

WHAT HAPPENED NEXT WAS ONE OF THE PIRATES STARTED STRUTTING UP AND DOWN IN FRONT OF US AND CUTTING OFF MEN'S EARS TO TERRIFY US.

EEW!

YEAH. EXCEPT, HE SLIPPED ON A WET ROPE AND FELL DOWN AND HIS GLASS EYE POPPED OUT.

TONK KRAAK

—EVERYBODY WAS TOO SCARED TO LAUGH; EVEN THE OTHER PIRATES, BECAUSE HE WAS THE BIGGEST ONE OF THEM ALL, AND THEIR FIRST MATE, I THINK.

EXCEPT I COULDN'T HELP IT, SO I LAUGHED RIGHT OUT LOUD AND EVERYBODY LOOKED AT ME.

—NOT THAT I THOUGHT IT WAS VERY FUNNY. —SEEING A GLASS EYE POP OUT ISN'T AS FUNNY AS IT SOUNDS.

IT DOESN'T EVEN SOUND FUNNY TO ME!

KRACK KRACK KRAK!

WHAT ARE YOU DOING IN THERE?

HA!

CRACKING WOOD AWAY FROM THE HINGES.

SO WHY DID YOU LAUGH?

—JUST TO MAKE HIM ANGRY?

YEAH. AND BECAUSE I WAS ANGRY.

PIRATES HAVE THICK SKIN, AND THEY DON'T LET MUCH GET TO THEM. —BUT I KNEW IT WOULD BUG HIM TO LAUGH WHEN NOBODY ELSE WAS BRAVE ENOUGH.

HOLD ON...

BUMP

ERK!

ooch!

SLITHER

≥ERK!≤ OUCH!

THUMP

HM.

IT'S HARDER TO MOVE AT THIS END.

ANYWAY, HE PICKED ME RIGHT UP AND I DON'T KNOW IF HE WAS GOING TO CUT MY EAR OFF OR JUST CUT MY THROAT AND KILL ME.

—BUT IT DIDN'T MATTER BECAUSE EVEN THOUGH THEY TIED UP MY FEET, I COULD STILL USE MY KNEES, SO I KNOCKED HIM!

HIS KNIFE WENT RIGHT INTO THE BOTTOM OF HIS CHIN. —RIGHT INTO HIS MOUTH FROM UNDERNEATH!

WHEN HE YELLED, IT CUT HIM EVEN MORE, SO HE COULDN'T EVEN MAKE A SOUND.

I THINK I MIGHT HAVE EVEN CUT HIS TONGUE IN HALF, BUT I NEVER FOUND OUT FOR SURE.

ANYWAY AFTER THAT HE WAS **SO** MAD, AND THAT'S WHEN HE THREW ME IN A TRUNK AND DUMPED IT OVERBOARD.

—THEY TIED THE SHIP'S ANCHOR TO IT FIRST, SO I'D SINK RIGHT TO THE BOTTOM!

WOW! BUT YOU GOT OUT THOUGH, RIGHT?

UH HUH.

I DIDN'T EVEN TRY TO OPEN THE LID. —I KICKED AT THE END INSTEAD. —I KICKED AND KICKED, AND I WAS LUCKY, BECAUSE THE SIDES WERE JUST NAILED AND NOT PROPERLY JOINTED.

—THE SIDES KICKED OUT EASILY.

BUT YOU WERE UNDER WATER!

YEAH. AND DEEP, TOO.

AND IT RUSHED IN THROUGH THE FIRST CRACK AND IT WAS COLD AND BLACK. —AND I ALMOST BREATHED IT IN!

I ALMOST PANICKED!

SCRAPE CRACK

WOW. I PROBABLY WOULD HAVE!

WELL I WAS LUCKY, BECAUSE I DIDN'T. —THE INSTANT I GOT FREE, I SWAM UP AND UP.

I'VE NEVER BEEN THAT DEEP BEFORE!

I SWAM UP AND UP, AND RIGHT WHEN I WAS COMPLETELY OUT OF BREATH AND JUST HAD TO BREATHE, THAT'S WHEN I BURST THROUGH THE SURFACE!

WOW!

YEAH.

SO WHAT HAPPENED THEN?

CRACK

WELL AFTER I CAUGHT MY BREATH, I SWAM BACK TO THE SHIP. LUCKILY, THERE WAS NO WIND AND I COULD SEE THEIR LIGHTS.

I SWAM BACK, AND CLIMBED UP THE SIDE AND GOT ON BOARD.

—I DID IT REALLY QUIETLY, AND I CUT MY GRANDFATHER AND THE REST OF THE CREW LOOSE, AND I SNUCK THEM WEAPONS AND STUFF, BACK AND FORTH UNTIL IT WAS NEARLY MORNING.

THEN WE ALL JUMPED UP AND TOOK THEM BY SURPRISE!

WE HAD THE UPPER HAND EVEN THOUGH THERE WERE MORE OF THEM THAN US. —AND MY GRANDFATHER KILLED THE ONE-EYED PIRATE WITH ONE PUNCH, HE WAS SO MAD!

HE HIT HIM ON THE CHIN AND HIS HEAD SNAPPED RIGHT BACK.

CRACK

WOW.

MY GRAND FATHER WAS REALLY STRONG.

AND YOU WON?

YUP.

CRACK CRICK

IT WAS REALLY SAD THAT WE LOST HALF OUR CREW.

SOME OF THEM KNEW EACH OTHER FOR A LONG TIME.

BUT, YEAH. —WE WERE PRETTY GLAD ABOUT WINNING.

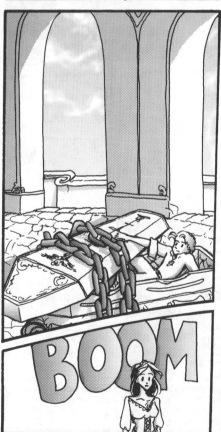

Varkias yawned.

"How long till you get to practice magic again?" he asked.

"Friday."

"How many days away is that?"

Heath sighed. "Three."

"Oh."

Heath continued pouring the strong smelling fluid from the keg into the smaller bottles, being careful not to spill. The kegs were heavy and it was very warm in the back room. She stopped briefly and put her hand on her hip.

"You know what I really hate about all this?" she fumed.

Varkias blinked at her. "What?"

"Well, I know I have to work here to earn my keep. —And I really like Mrs. Zelga, and Jenny. They've both been really nice to me. And I even like this job. But I know inside what I really *should* be doing. I should be practicing my magic! Except I'm not spending *nearly* enough time on it!"

"Yeah, and you promised the king you'd help fight Locumire and then go back and rescue him from the Dragon's Dream."

"Exactly!" She exclaimed, and then paused thoughtfully. "Actually, I sort of forgot about that. I *did* promise, didn't I?"

"That's what happens if you spend too long acting like regular people."

"Argh! That's what I mean! I feel stuck in *between*." Heath paced in a tight circle. "I've got a mission! But I can't quit my job. I don't know what to *do."*

Varkias frowned. "Quinton never had to work. He never had a job in his life."

"Yeah. I noticed that."

"Nobody's crazy enough to hire him," Varkias said matter of factly, "Plus he's a big mooch."

"Well, I'm not a big mooch! Quinton's different, so it works out for him. But I'm *me*. Trisha Ringlet says in the book that everybody's different. If you see somebody who's got a way that works, you can try as hard as you want, but you'll never be able to copy it. You've gotta come up with your *own* way."

"Rubel also says stuff like that. . ."

"Yeah, except he seems to be able to make it work." Heath sighed again.

"Rubel is pretty cool," Varkias agreed.

"Hrm. Well, that's what I've got to do as well! Because what I'm doing now is getting me nowhere. Except *here.*"

Varkias looked about the small room.

"I am *positive,*" Heath continued, waxing dramatic, "that I am wasting precious time. There are a lot of really *important* things going on; with the prince and Locumire and the king, and I *know* I'm supposed to be a part of it, but instead I'm not being any help at all!"

She sighed conclusively and said nothing more. It was a problem with which she had been struggling for many days now.

HEY! I KNOW!

WHY DON'T YOU USE A **SPELL** TO DO YOUR WORK **FOR** YOU?

-YOU COULD FILL ALL THESE BOTTLES BY **MAGIC**!

UG! YOU CAN'T DO THAT!

WHY NOT? YOU'D GET YOUR CHORES DONE AND BE PRACTICING MAGIC AT THE SAME TIME.

NO WAY! ARE YOU CRAZY? -THERE'S **HUNDREDS** OF STORIES ABOUT APPRENTICES WHO TRY STUFF LIKE THAT!

SOMETHING **ALWAYS** GOES WRONG!

REALLY? HOW COME?

WELL, BECAUSE IT...

UM...

HM.

I DON'T KNOW EXACTLY. IT JUST SORT OF DOES.

PFT. SEEMS STUPID TO ME. -BESIDES, IF YOU DON'T PRACTICE ON THE SIMPLE STUFF, HOW ARE YOU GOING TO LEARN TO DO ANYTHING DIFFICULT?

ACTUALLY, IT DOES SOUND KIND OF STUPID.

THEY MAKE UP STORIES LIKE THAT JUST TO STOP DUMB PEOPLE FROM GETTING AHEAD. -BEING SMART ENOUGH TO BREAK THE RULES IS LIKE PASSING A **TEST.**

I'M GOING TO LOOK FOR A SPELL!

WHAT IS THIS STUFF, ANYWAY.

LAMP IGNITER FLUID.

OKAY, I'VE GOT ONE. BE QUIET.

IS IT WORKING?

NO. MY MIND IS ALL JUMBLED.

IT'S BEEN LIKE THIS EVER SINCE I TRIED THAT FIRST SPELL.

THE 'FIND IT' SPELL? MAYBE THAT FIRST TIME WAS BEGINNER'S LUCK.

HM... YEAH...

HM.

ACTUALLY, I THINK IT MIGHT BE WORSE. I THINK IT HAS TO DO WITH ME WORKING HERE AND GOING TO SCHOOL AND TRYING TO BE NORMAL.

THAT'S WHAT I'M ALL WORRIED ABOUT. I GOT THE FEELING THE MAGIC WAS TESTING ME.

TESTING YOU?

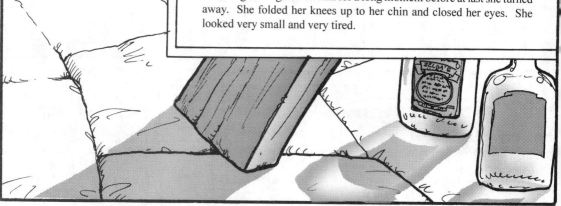

Heath sat down, troubled. "I don't know. All I know is that I haven't been able to make a single spell work at all since that day. And I don't even know *how* I got those first spells to work. I didn't know what I was doing. Maybe I'm just not trying hard enough now. Or maybe I'm trying *too* hard. I've been practicing every night really late, but nothing works at all. I don't know. I can't figure it out. It's like everything I do is just leading me further and further away. . ."

She found herself struck then with a wave of real worry which sank to the bottom of her stomach, heavy and cold. She turned to face the imp, her eyebrows knitting, and confided in a small voice, "I'm not sure what to do, Varkias. What if I never figure it out? What if I really am not good enough? What if I *do* become normal?"

The shadow settling across her face grew as she considered this possibility truly and honestly for the first time. She had been telling herself for days now that it was just one of those things which came and went, like a bad mood, or a touch of forgetfulness which would surely pass and needn't be worried over. After all, she was the *Red Sorceress;* Quinton had discovered her. But. . , there was also the matter of Katara, her other self who perhaps of the two of them was destined to take all the magic and leave her with nothing. Quinton was still missing, and her life in this city was . . . well, she wasn't so sure about anything anymore.

Varkias, not knowing any of the right things friends were supposed to say at such moments as these, uttered a small sound but nothing else. Heath's gaze lingered on him for a long moment before at last she turned away. She folded her knees up to her chin and closed her eyes. She looked very small and very tired.

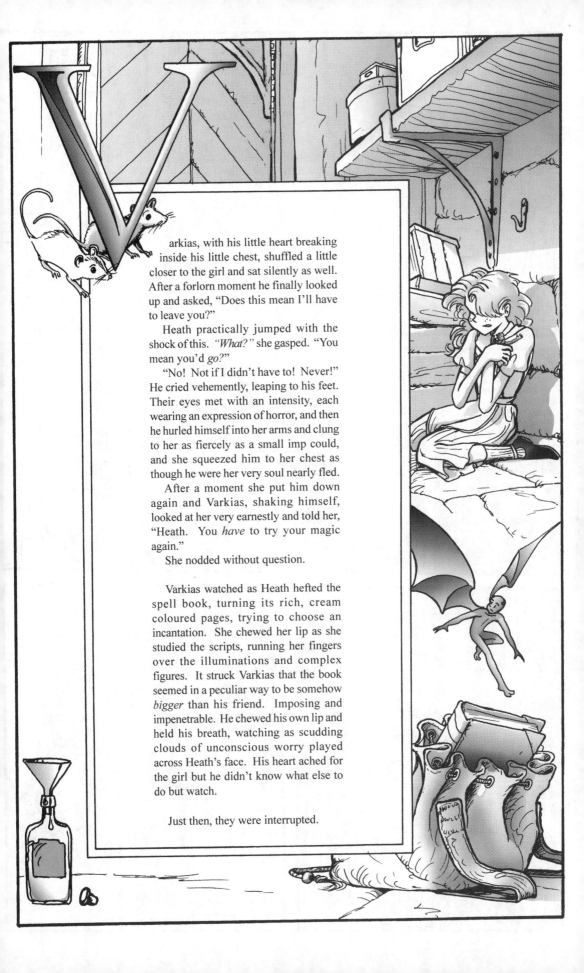

arkias, with his little heart breaking inside his little chest, shuffled a little closer to the girl and sat silently as well. After a forlorn moment he finally looked up and asked, "Does this mean I'll have to leave you?"

Heath practically jumped with the shock of this. *"What?"* she gasped. "You mean you'd *go?*"

"No! Not if I didn't have to! Never!" He cried vehemently, leaping to his feet. Their eyes met with an intensity, each wearing an expression of horror, and then he hurled himself into her arms and clung to her as fiercely as a small imp could, and she squeezed him to her chest as though he were her very soul nearly fled.

After a moment she put him down again and Varkias, shaking himself, looked at her very earnestly and told her, "Heath. You *have* to try your magic again."

She nodded without question.

Varkias watched as Heath hefted the spell book, turning its rich, cream coloured pages, trying to choose an incantation. She chewed her lip as she studied the scripts, running her fingers over the illuminations and complex figures. It struck Varkias that the book seemed in a peculiar way to be somehow *bigger* than his friend. Imposing and impenetrable. He chewed his own lip and held his breath, watching as scudding clouds of unconscious worry played across Heath's face. His heart ached for the girl but he didn't know what else to do but watch.

Just then, they were interrupted.

MAYBE YOU WERE LUCKY.

SHE LOOKED LIKE SHE MIGHT HAVE BEEN DANGEROUS.

BUT DID YOU HEAR WHAT SHE SAID?

SHE SAID THERE WAS NOTHING HERE OF ANY *USE*.

DO YOU THINK SHE WAS TALKING ABOUT *ME*?

WHAT IF SHE CAME BECAUSE SHE WAS LOOKING FOR A GREAT SORCERESS, AND SHE FOUND *ME* INSTEAD?

SHE COULD TELL I HAVEN'T GOT ANY MAGIC!

ARGH!!

SHE COULD TELL I WAS *USELESS!*

THAT IS *IT*.

I'M *SICK* OF THIS!

I'M DONE MESSING AROUND!

COME ON, VARKIAS. WE'RE DOING SOME *MAGIC*.

Chapter 6

ACK!

MUROMA FIE ASIGMA, TRISHA RINGLET LU!

STAY BEHIND US, GIRL.

BREATHE DEEPLY. REMAIN ALOOF.

YOU DO NOT MAKE SMALL NOISES WHEN YOU MOVE! FIRST YOU KNOCK DOWN A **MOUNTAIN SIDE** AND NOW YOU CONJURE UP A <u>WIND</u>!

STAY BACK BUT KEEP EYE-CONTACT WITH IT. —IF YOU KEEP YOUR EYES ON ITS, IT CANNOT HARM US.

I DID NOT THINK IT TO LOOK AT YOU!

WE WILL TRY TO DISPELL WHAT YOU HAVE DONE.

WE SHOULD ERASE THE DAMAGE FROM THE WIND'S PASSAGE.
—WE CAN'T HAVE LOCUMIRE'S GIRLS DISCOVERING US.

NO. NOT YET.
COME ALONG, CHILD. —WHAT IS YOUR NAME?

HEATH. —HEATH WINGWHIT, MA'AM.

THANK YOU...

WINGWHIT. BUT OF COURSE.

MY NAME IS **CALYPSO**.
AND THIS IS **CATASTROPHE**.

AT YOUR SERVICE, HEATH WINGWHIT.

AND YOURS TOO, VARKIAS. IT HAS BEEN A LONG TIME.

YOU ARE INVISIBLE TO MORTALS, AND TO MILEENA, BUT I CAN SEE WITH AURIL'S EYE.

YOUR MEMORY HAS ALWAYS BEEN SHORT.

YIKE!

COME ON. —WE MUST PUT THINGS STRAIGHT AND GET YOU BACK TO WHERE YOU WILL NOT BE NOTICED.

QUITE!

CATASTROPHE?

Meanwhile. . , somewhere along the river Vine and tow road, there sits beneath the imposing shadow of the Sleeping Wood, the small royalist supply wharf of *Palvincia*. —Too small to be called a town, long forgotten treaties stand between the kingdom of Asaria and the Wood; forgotten, but still silently adhered to. Palvencia will never be more than a tolerated stone at the foot of that vast and towering realm. . .

Openly having confronted Locumire, and worse, after having *defeated* her, Soracia was on the run. Locumire, furious after having suffered such a humiliation, swore as so many countless villains had done before, that she would stop at *nothing*. And so she set about in all her clever and vile ways to recapture Soracia and to put her back in her place, where if truth be told, Soracia had never really been. Knowing this made Locumire seeth with hatred. She would stop at *nothing!*

Of course, Soracia was not one to be trifled with. Afer all, she was the dark and dangerous Shadow Lady, and her lord and master held powers beyond mortal comprehension. —Soracia wore a cloak made from the cuttings of *his* very shadow, and she wielded mysterious weapons forged by *his* very hands, made from materials more mysterious still; swords which danced at her finger tips and did her will without question. Such gifts were his to grant, and giving them to Soracia had been his bittersweet pleasure, for though she held a mortal heart and thus some of Quinton's touch, she was dark and beautiful and tragic, and so had been his favorite since the dawn of his reign. Locumire, while she had seen her thousandth birthday only a few short years ago, remained barely a sapling in his eyes.

Though Soracia had been distant recently. Dissatisfied and restless. She had been asking difficult, heartfelt questions and she had not been following the instructions of his ministers, (which was nothing new, but this time he could sense something different in her attitude.) —Now, it was true, Soracia always strayed somewhat during those millennia where she remained awake while he was forced to sleep. Leaving her to her own ends for hundreds of years at a time was sure to cause her to slip from her true path. But this time. . .

Well, this time was different.

Lucille Locumire, on the other hand, was dependent on him. Her immortality sprang from his coffers of power, and her magic over the mortal world coursed from his heart. She did not forget for whom she lived. And so Ramanious placed into her hands the task of gathering up his wayward queen and returning her to his side. And Locumire, angry and loyal, though hating Soracia, set to the task with vigor.

Thus, Lord Ramanious, shaking off the mantle of his thousand year sleep, bore the weight of his great mind forth into the world beyond, seeking the hot shard of soul within Soracia over which he held command. The shard of his *own* soul.

Through the kingdom of Oceansend, from which his new empire was beginning to flower, his mind's eye roved, out across the vast fields and orchards which would soon feed his clamoring armies. Oceansend would be his jewel. It had risen before to oppose him when his armies had come from the south, but this time he would make it his. The strengths it held would serve *him*, he would see to it, and this time there would be no hero Telenvoe to rally armies against him. Nor a traveler Progenis to pry at his secrets. Quinton's Nove-blooded thief was half the way to belonging to *him* without the boy even realizing it! —An old plan hatched by Soracia herself. If not for Soracia's change of heart and her recent interference, Rubel would have already freed the beast, Chead, from the stone box in which it was kept, and then all the pieces of Ramanious' war stratagem would be in place.

But he needed Soracia back.

He found her, naturally, hiding in the Sleeping Wood, the one remaining place where his vision was still obscured. The Wood would burn this time. He swore it. Anger at old memories rose hot within him, but as though the Wood could barely even bother to make the effort, it shrugged away his attempts at penetration as though he were a child.

His ties to Soracia, however, were of the deepest, most unbreakable sort. Like the invisible threads which connect true lovers no matter where they are, his hold over her was a malefic cable, and the dismissive interference of the Wood caused his pent up rage to boil. Though he could not see her, Soracia convulsed and cried out through the darkness as his mind filled hers. She shrieked, and the elaborate magic she had been trying to cast shattered at the touch of his mind. She turned to flee, and her blind race took her from the wood. To its very edge. To Palvencia.

And in her madness, she laid waste to it all.

BOOM BOOM BOOM

WELL, HERE WE GO...

SHADOW QUEEN! ORDERS FOR YOUR ARREST, HAVE I!

WAIT FOR IT...

SHOP!

ROAR

NO

I SUSPECTED AS MUCH!

LITTLE CESPINARVE!

SO THE DRAGON LIKES HEATH. —EVEN LOVES HER, PERHAPS.

HE STOOD UP FOR HER WHERE SHE COULD NOT, AND YOU COULDN'T STOP HIM.

I SEE!

HA! BALLYRAGS LIKE YOU ARE ALWAYS ASHAMED WHEN THE ONES YOU TORMENT TURN AND DEFEAT YOU WITH ONLY HALF AN EFFORT.

IT TERRIFIES YOU TO THINK THAT ROGUE HAS FOR ALL THIS TIME BEEN STRONG ENOUGH TO FACE YOU BUT HAS SIMPLY NEVER BOTHERED.

YOU'RE THE WEAK AND STUPID ONE, GORGON!

LYING TO RAMANIOUS WON'T CHANGE THAT!

NOOOOoo

NOoo! LITTLE WORM IS WEAK!

NASTY, NASTY WORM! —IS *NOT* STRONG ENOUGH TO STOP **KLACHILIES**! NOT *ME*!

NOoooo!

PFT.

YOU'RE PATHETIC.

EITHER WAY, I'M NOT SURPRISED HEATH GOT PAST YOU. —SHE'S MY *SISTER*, AFTER ALL.

SISTER...?

THAT'S RIGHT.

OH, AND YOU'RE GOING TO GET IN TROUBLE WHEN I TELL HOW YOU LIED.

RAMANIOUS ALWAYS THOUGHT YOU WERE *SO* TRUSTWORTHY.

HE'LL PROBABLY CAST YOU BACK TO THE EARTH HE PULLED YOU FROM!

YOU'LL LIVE NO MORE WHEN I TELL HIM THE TRUTH!

OOOO!

HE WOULD! HE WOULD

SO DISAPPOINTED WOULD HE BE!

SO *TERRIBLE* AND *WONDERFUL* IS HE!

Chapter 7

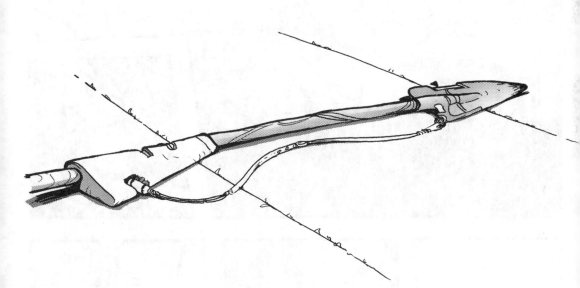

NAH!

SO ARE YOU TELLING ME YOU HAD A **SECRET TUNNEL** ALL THIS TIME!

YUP!

WELL IF YOU HAD THAT, WHY DID HAVE TO YOU GO AND TRICK **ME** INTO LETTING YOU OUT THE OTHER DAY?!

EVERYBODY THOUGHT I WAS A SPY!

EVERYBODY THOUGHT I WAS A TRAITOR!

OH, WELL I ONLY JUST REMEMBERED ABOUT THE TUNNEL THIS MORNING.

YOU **FORGOT**?!

YEAH, I KNOW.

SEEMS UNUSUAL FOR A MIND OF SUCH PIERCING INTELLECT AS MINE TO FORGET ANYTHING.

BUT YESTERDAY I REALIZED WHAT IT MUST BE.

I BELIEVE I MUST HAVE USED SOME KIND OF DANGEROUSLY ADVANCED MEDITATIVE TECHNIQUE, -THE NATURE OF WHICH I CAN NO LONGER RECALL- TO BLOCK VITAL DATA FROM MY MEMORY.

-IN ORDER TO HAMPER ANY **INTERROGATION** ATTEMPTS MY ENEMIES MIGHT USE!

I EXPECT I'LL ONLY REMEMBER THINGS AS THEY BECOME NECESSARY TO PROGRESS THE VARIOUS STAGES OF MY MASTER PLAN.

IT WAS PART OF YOUR "**MASTER PLAN**" TO MAKE IT LOOK LIKE I WAS BETRAYING THE **PRINCESS?!**

I'M SURE OF IT.

YOU'RE THE PERFECT FOOT SOLDIER IN THE UNENDING WAR AGAINST EVIL.

YOU'RE STOUT-HEARTED AND EASILY LED; READY TO GIVE YOUR LIFE AT A MOMENT'S NOTICE!

NATURALLY I HAD TO HAVE YOU ON MY SIDE.

I'M VERY FORTUNATE THINGS WORKED OUT AS THEY DID, OR I'D HAVE NEVER MANAGED TO WIN YOU OVER!

BUT I NEVER

EITHER WAY, I NEED A NEW APPRENTICE. -MY OLD ONE LOCKED ME UP.

SHE SAID I WAS SELF-CENTERED AND MANIPULATIVE.

HEY! SEE?

—BENEATH MY LUMINARY GUIDANCE, YOU'VE ALREADY BEGUN TO PROBE BEYOND THE BAFFLING RIDDLES OF THE UNIVERSE WHICH ARE INCOMPREHENSIBLE TO NORMAL BRAINS!

YOU'LE MAKE A GREAT SORCERER ONE DAY!

NOW JUST YOU HOLD ON —

SHH!

OKAY! NOW YOU HAVE TO PUSH UP ON THIS STONE.

WHAT?

NATURAL EROSION WILL HAVE FILLED SOME OF THE SLIDE-WAYS WITH DIRT, BUT YOU'VE GOT TROLL-STRENGTH.

WAIT A MOMENT FOR THEM TO GET A LITTLE FURTHER...

OKAY! NOW!

ULP!

WELL! THAT TAKES CARE OF OUR PURSUERS!

WHAT HAPPENED?! WHAT **WAS** THAT?!

AUTOMATIC SIEGE DEFENCE.

WHEN I DESIGNED THIS PLACE FOR PRINCE JEHOSA, I INCLUDED A NUMBER OF REMOTE INITIATORS; STRICTLY OFF THE BOOKS, OF COURSE. —THAT LITTLE CAVE WAS ONE OF THEM.

IT HAD A BIG STONE DOOR WHEN IT WAS BUILT, BUT I MADE SURE THE HINGES WERE MADE FROM IRON RATHER THAN STONE PIVOTS. —I NEEDED THEM TO BE RUSTED AWAY SO THE DOOR WOULD BE GONE FOR TODAY.

YOU **PLANNED** FOR THIS..?

WELL, I CAN'T BE EXPECTED TO IMPROVISE ALL THE TIME. NOBODY'S PERFECT!

COME ON. LET'S DOUBLE BACK AND GET OUT OF HERE!

WE CAN'T HOPE TO HIDE LONG FROM KATARA. THE FOREST LOVES HER TOO WELL, SO WE'LL JUST RUN FLAT OUT TO THE WEST. —NO CAT AND MOUSING ABOUT!

SHE'LL HAVE SEEN THE SMOKE ALREADY FROM MY BURNING BUSH TRICK, AND SHE'LL HAVE GUESSED WHAT'S GOING ON.

BUT INSTEAD OF COMING AFTER ME RIGHT AWAY, SHE'LL HEAD BACK TO CAMP TO MAKE SURE EVERYBODY'S OKAY.

SO, JUST AS LONG AS NOTHING STOPS US, WE'LL BE ABLE TO—

OH,
RIGHT.

YOU
GUYS.

lachilies strained at the world with his new eyes.

"*Most* strange," he repeated for the fifth time as he trailed through the air beside Soracia. The Shadow Lady did not reply as she made her way over the stone path. After some hesitation he added, "Why does it *look* so as it does. . ? It is not as it looked before."

Soracia did not turn as she answered. "The eyes I gave you were taken from a man you once turned to stone. Men see in color, and now you do as well."

"Color. . ." Klachilies was silent for a space and then asked, "You also see this way? The world with color?"

"Yes."

"All of the time?"

"Yes. Men and women see the world in color."

Klachilies mulled quietly over this for some time before repeating once more with resolution, "It is *most* strange." As they passed an apple tree, he turned to gaze up through the tangled proliferation of reds and greens set against the bright blue of the sky. "Most strange is it to serve a Shadow Sister!"

After a twisty distance through a labyrinth of pathways and walls and clipped bushes, the scenery changed abruptly. The garden architecture, stairways, walls and arches, all grew large and broad, pitching their way skyward with dreamy elegance.

"Hm." Soracia frowned.

"It is not as it was," Klachilies observed. "More than color, this is!"

Soracia stood for a moment with narrowed eyes.

All which existed in the garden did so because the dragon, Cespinarve Rogue, dreamed it; the *world magic* from which he was made caused the notions in his sleep to take on dimensions that normal people's dreams did not. But even beyond this, his dream garden was unusual; even for a World Dragon.

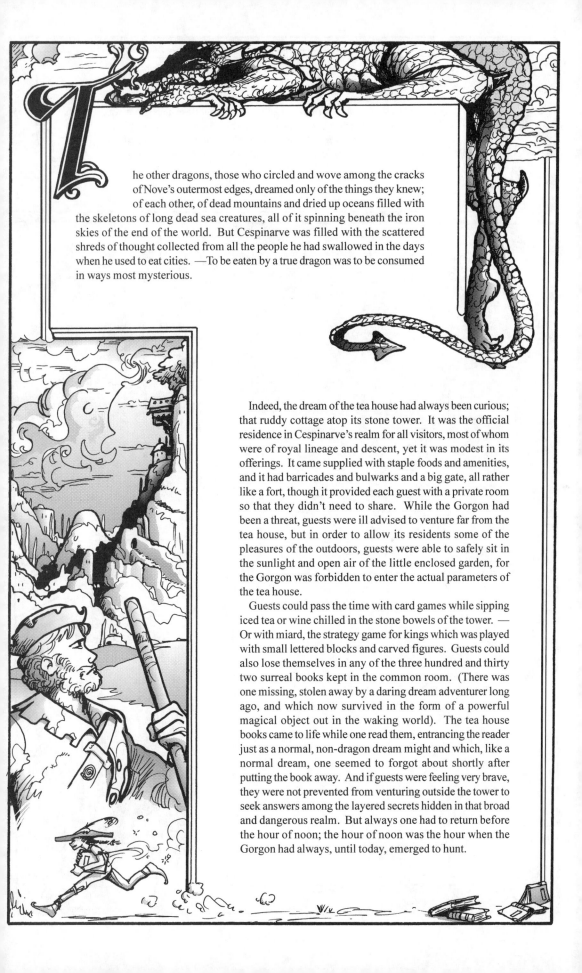

he other dragons, those who circled and wove among the cracks of Nove's outermost edges, dreamed only of the things they knew; of each other, of dead mountains and dried up oceans filled with the skeletons of long dead sea creatures, all of it spinning beneath the iron skies of the end of the world. But Cespinarve was filled with the scattered shreds of thought collected from all the people he had swallowed in the days when he used to eat cities. —To be eaten by a true dragon was to be consumed in ways most mysterious.

Indeed, the dream of the tea house had always been curious; that ruddy cottage atop its stone tower. It was the official residence in Cespinarve's realm for all visitors, most of whom were of royal lineage and descent, yet it was modest in its offerings. It came supplied with staple foods and amenities, and it had barricades and bulwarks and a big gate, all rather like a fort, though it provided each guest with a private room so that they didn't need to share. While the Gorgon had been a threat, guests were ill advised to venture far from the tea house, but in order to allow its residents some of the pleasures of the outdoors, guests were able to safely sit in the sunlight and open air of the little enclosed garden, for the Gorgon was forbidden to enter the actual parameters of the tea house.

Guests could pass the time with card games while sipping iced tea or wine chilled in the stone bowels of the tower. — Or with miard, the strategy game for kings which was played with small lettered blocks and carved figures. Guests could also lose themselves in any of the three hundred and thirty two surreal books kept in the common room. (There was one missing, stolen away by a daring dream adventurer long ago, and which now survived in the form of a powerful magical object out in the waking world). The tea house books came to life while one read them, entrancing the reader just as a normal, non-dragon dream might and which, like a normal dream, one seemed to forgot about shortly after putting the book away. And if guests were feeling very brave, they were not prevented from venturing outside the tower to seek answers among the layered secrets hidden in that broad and dangerous realm. But always one had to return before the hour of noon; the hour of noon was the hour when the Gorgon had always, until today, emerged to hunt.

What was how the tea house had been for countless ages, so it was with some consternation that Soracia walked among the new pillars and fountains, no longer recognizing the surroundings she had known for several millennium's worth of visits. She no longer recognized it, but she suspected. . .

It was not long until they arrived before a florid gentleman in butler's garb, who bowed deeply to them.

"Your Excellence!" he greeted with the practiced respect of a well trained servant, but who clearly was making an effort to control his excitement. "I cannot *tell* you how humbled we all are by your presence." He cast a halting glance at Kalchilies, and his face paled slightly. "Even vanquished," he breathed, "it looks. . . But of course, he is in your care! We need not fear, none of us, so long as you are here, your Majesty!"

"I have come to see the kings," Soracia told him. "I would see them without delay."

"And their Excellencies wish to see you! The kings wish to meet you that you may together enjoy the parade in your honor."

"Very well. Please lead the way."

The florid gentleman beamed at her, "Yes, my Lady! This way," he said, controlling the emotion in his voice and turned to lead Soracia onward, although his chest puffed out as though this were the proudest moment of his life.

"A parade?" Klachilies asked. "A parade is what?"

"A celebration in the form of a choreographed march," Soracia answered.

"A celebration?"

Soracia remained silent as she walked.

Faces began to appear alongside the path they were following. Boys and girls and men and women, pretty and pudgy, clad in luxurious, relaxed garments, and some not, all looking as though they had plopped down from one of those lush paintings of ages gone where naked women bathed and ate grapes. They peeked shyly at Soracia, and fearfully at the gorgon, their emotions utterly plain on their faces. Soracia regarded them impassively.

Their guide snapped his fingers at them. "Tut, tut!" he scolded. "Make way for the Queen! Make way for the *Queen!* Really!" he looked apologetically over his shoulder. "Many hundreds of pardons, your Highness. There really ought to be an escort to shoo away this rabble! To shuffle off these braggarts! To harry these peons away! Tut, tut! These upstarts and rough bullies!" He stamped his foot at a very small boy who squeaked and ran to hide behind a bright tulip. "This unwashed mob! This crass hoard!"

"The kings," Soracia reminded patiently. "My time here is short."

"Quite, your Excellence! Quite. I apologize most emphatically. Ah!" his face brightened. "Our escort has arrived."

A band of majestically colored soldiers marched into view and stood at attention.

"Proceed. Proceed!" their guide directed archly. "We will have an orderly progression now. Here, here! Make way for the Queen!" He strutted boldly, and the armed soldiers marched, flanking them, their feet working in perfect time. Klachilies observed them curiously, and one or two of them flickered worried eyes back at him. After a short distance, another dozen guardsmen joined their band. "Yes, excellent!" their guide exclaimed. "Make way for the Queen! Make way for the Tamer of the Gorgon! For *she* who has *delivered us from tribulation!*"

As this unusual spectacle clattered along, the surrounding landscape became increasingly more robust and exotic, pillars and bushes soaring higher and ever more triumphant than those before, while the pathway grew wider and its paving stones lighter and shinier, flecked with silver and gold. Every hundred steps, another contingent of decorated soldiers arrived, their chins held high with the sun dancing on their armor and their glittering badges and ribbons of honor tousling with each step. As they proceeded, their numbers grew, each rank falling behind the last in correct marching order so that it began to look as though Soracia was leading a small army.

Mounted cavalry soon joined them, their horses rife with streamers and ribbons trailing from their proud manes and armor, while resplendent flags flapped gaily from the high points of their rider's lances. Then all at once, as though the floodgates were overcome with happiness, elephants and drum beaters and flute players and golden carriages drawing blushing princesses joined their march while the thousands of ecstatic faces now lining the fairway looked on in sheer delight.

The procession mounted a hill, and at its crest, they could see the valley below. The tea house grounds had increased considerably. Before them the course of the fairway wove an impossibly tangled and curving path, and hundreds of thousands of enthusiastic, happy figures could be seen with their faces turned up from the valley below to witness their approach, a thunderous cheer rising to meet them as the parade became visible. The sky wavered huge and dreamily overhead, and in the distance, their destination was clear; a gleaming white and gold palace shining on the horizon.

"Ah! Many colors there are involved!" Klachilies said, with a tremor of his own strange emotion.

A flicker of impatience crossed Soracia's expression.

"This dream is frightened. The labyrinth is stirring," she said. "I suspect Rogue has an inkling of why I have come."

"Smash it all to pieces, could I. .," the gorgon offered.

"No. Rogue would be able to strike back and kill you now."

"Defeat me?"

"No. Kill you. Entirely. His self confidence has grown since your last encounter. And if he were to kill you, I believe there is a good chance he might wake up. —You have been the primary challenge of this dream for a long time. We must allow a natural shift to another mood, or all will be concluded and there will be no further reason for his sleep to continue. I do not know what would happen if he were to wake up while we are still this deep within his mind. My work is here is growing critical."

Their guide had been carried so far away on his personal wave of euphoria and self importance that he did not hear these comments, but continued to strut with his chest puffed out so far that it looked as though he might be in danger of tipping over backwards. As the parade marched on, the palace slipped out of sight behind a high wall. When it returned into view, it seemed further off than before.

"Will not reach it, I think. If it fears us it will always be far," the gorgon observed.

Soracia looked skyward. "I must risk flight. Luckily I am only poisoned and not bleeding; I will not drain of life quite so quickly today. Follow."

he leaped up and sailed into the air, leaving the sputtering dream guide behind them.

"What. . ? But! *But, your Highness!*"

He was drowned out by the crowd, which gasped in a collective awe that sounded like the wind, for it almost was.

The palace was indeed avoiding the pair. It swam for the horizon while the rest of the dream realm waxed hazy and confusing in an attempt to misdirect their attention. But Soracia could be as cold and humorless as ice when she needed to be, not one to be misled by such tricks, and Klachilies had no

trouble keeping pace with her; the gorgon had spent most of its existence as a dream beast and so knew the ways of the dragon's mind. Thus the pair drew slowly upon the shining palace through that tug o' war of scurrying perceptions. After some time of this, however, as though it knew the battle was indeed lost, the palace relented and rushed up to them with a vehemence. Its gold and silver spires spun vertiginously beneath them, huge spikes threatening into the air, daring them to land. With some concentration, Soracia denied herself the slippery mental slope which would have allowed those towering daggers to become a real danger, and twirled gracefully down through them to light upon the old and worn paving stones which led as they always had, up to the tea house tower.

Klachilies hung back.

"The dragon will not let me," the gorgon said. "This place is strong for him. His centre cannot be ruined."

The elaborate sign placard which always stood before the tower now informed them in black letters of painted tar that Gorgons and Shadow Queens were by no means whatever permitted to enter King's Crossing on pain of death. Soracia flung a pale hand up before the placard, her fingers spread wide, and the wooden post and hanging boards roared into a sudden, angry blaze. The tarry letters smoked thick and black, sizzling.

"These hectic days are a time for breaking old rules and casting new ones, Klachilies. These are days of the reckless and the brave."

"Which are we?" Klachilies asked, approaching cautiously.

"You are neither. You do not crave self determination above all things, and so your lot is to always follow. To find a bright soul in whom to lay your adoration and trust."

"Oh. . ." The gorgon hung motionless in the air for a time as it considered this. "And what lot is yours?" he asked.

"Mine. . ." Soracia pondered a moment before the blaze. Surrounded by the palace walls which had replaced the huge stone rampart Quinton had somehow suggested into existence, the old tea house was as ruddy and creaky as it had always been. She turned her chin up and squinted past the fire into the sunlight reflecting from the cottage windows.

Leading the way, Soracia drew a sword and brought it down in a single arc upon the lock of the tower gate, cutting it in half with a satisfying, 'Ping!' —The impediment of the gate which she had always before respected, had as well only been symbolic. The whole tower shuddered and groaned as she and Klachilies entered amidst the last shafts of sunlight, while the sky in the distance began to darken and rumble, going the color of iron.

The kings were found in the common room, waiting anxiously.

"We knew you were coming," said Fularo through his curled moustache, his hand gripped tightly on the hilt of his sword.

"Yes," said Rillion, standing. "*Do* come in."

MEANWHILE, IN THE ABANDONED **SUNKEN CITY**, RUBEL MARCHES ALONG...

WELL! YOU LOOK LIKE A SMALL ARMY!

YEAH. —MELISSA AND LAUROL GOT ALL THIS STUFF OUT OF THE RIVER FOR ME.

HE NEEDED MAGICAL WEAPONS. WE CAME BACK HERE TO GET OUR SPECIAL THINGS.

RUBEL HAS TO RESCUE A GIRL BEING HELD BY SUPERIOR FORCES!

YOU DO?

HER NAME IS KIM.

IT'S SHORT FOR KIMITHIN. SHE'S REALLY PRETTY AND REALLY NICE. —SHE WAS GOING TO HELP HIM ESCAPE FROM A COFFIN, BUT HE DIDN'T WANT TO GET HER IN TROUBLE.

HE LIKES HER A LOT!

HE WAS TELLING US ALL ABOUT IT.

A COFFIN?

SPLASH

HERE IT IS!

THIS IS WHAT I WAS TELLING YOU ABOUT!

IT'S THE MOST IMPORTANT THING OF ALL. IT'S AN AMULET. IT'LL MAKE IT SO YOU CAN'T GET SHOT. —ARROWS WILL GLANCE RIGHT OFF YOU!

I'LL GO GET MY RING!

SPLASH!

WOW. ARROWS WILL BOUNCE OFF ME IF I WEAR THIS?

WELL, NOT EXACTLY...

THEY GLANCE OFF. —IF THEY DON'T COME AT YOU STRAIGHT, THAT IS. —IF THEY'RE COMING AT YOU STRAIGHT, THEN IT'S NOT REALLY MUCH USE.

IT'S BETTER IF YOU AVOID BEING AT RIGHT ANGLES.

OH.

NOT TOO MANY GIRLS WOULD NEED SUCH AN ARSENAL FOR YOU TO PAY A VISIT.

HMM. SHE WOULDN'T ACTUALLY HAPPEN TO BE A WITCH, WOULD SHE?

UM.., YEAH, —BUT SHE'S REALLY NICE.

ONE OF LOCUMIRE'S GIRLS?

AND SHE'S HIS AGE AND EVERYTHING. TALKING WITH HER WAS REALLY EASY. —IT'S LIKE THEY JUST NATURALLY FIT!

IT'S LIKE THEY WERE MADE FOR EACH OTHER.

OH, RUBEL... YOU SHOULD BE MUCH MORE CAREFUL. —THOUGH, I SUPPOSE IT'S BETTER THAN IF YOU HAD MET A REGULAR GIRL.

YOU REALIZE NOW THAT ANYONE YOU FALL IN LOVE WITH IS AT GREAT RISK BECAUSE OF SORACIA.

OOH. —THE QUEEN OF HALVES WOULD GET REALLY JEALOUS. —SHE MIGHT KILL HER.

IT'S BECAUSE THEY KISSED THAT DAY

YEAH, BUT WHAT WAS HE SUPPOSED TO DO? —HE'S A THIEF AND ALL, AND THE QUEEN OF HALVES CAN LURE ANY MAN.

AND ESPECIALLY SINCE SHE'S IN LOVE WITH HIM...

WELL, NOT YET, SHE ISN'T.

SHE JUST HAS PLANS.

NO. LOVE IS LOVE!

NO. I'M TELLING YOU! SHE'S WAITING FOR HIM TO GET OLDER. —LIKE EIGHTEEN OR SO.

—AND THEN YOU BETTER WATCH OUT. —EITHER YOU FALL IN LOVE WITH HER COMPLETELY, OR START RUNNING NOW, CUZ SHE'LL BE REALLY MAD IF YOU FALL IN LOVE WITH SOMEBODY ELSE!

WELL, THAT MIGHT BE HOW SHE USED TO BE, BUT THINGS ARE DIFFERENT NOW.

SHE JUST NEEDS FRIENDS, AND I'M GOING TO BE HER'S. —AND ANYWAY, WHEN I FIGURE IT ALL OUT, I'LL BE ABLE TO MAKE EVERYTHING WORK OUT FOR HER.

ANYHOW, I HAVE TO GET GOING! —I HAVE TO VISIT HEATH!

THANKS FOR ALL THE STUFF!

BYE! BYE RUBEL!

HE SURE SEEMS TO RUN AROUND A LOT. —HE'S TRYING TO DO SOMETHING FOR EVERYBODY!

YEAH. EXCEPT FOR SARA. HE DOESN'T EVEN TRY PICKING HER LOCK ANYMORE.

SIGH.

Chapter 8

SIGH...

YOW! SHE'S LOOKING RIGHT AT ME!

I'M SUPPOSED TO BE INVISIBLE!

MARTHE? IS THAT YOU?

YIKES! LEAVE ME ALONE!

MARTHE?

CRAZY OLD LADY!

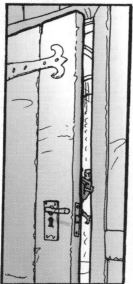

CLIK

I DON'T GET WHY YOU'RE SO ANGRY!

eath measured Rubel with her expression.

"So this Kim girl. . . She was the only one guarding you when you escaped from the coffin? And she didn't warn the others?"

"No," Rubel reassured quickly. "She knew she should have, but she's really nice. It's obvious that Locumire tricked her into being on their side."

Heath did not look convinced.

"Obvious? How is it *obvious*?"

"Oh, I could tell from the moment I met her. It's the way she talks about things. She was even going to help me escape before they put me in the coffin, but her friend came back at the last moment." Rubel's face darkened. "Her friend is a total psycho. I think most of Locumire's witches are."

"And you think this Kim is the only nice one?"

"As far as I can tell."

"And they kept leaving you alone with her? And that's how you started to like her?" Heath's eyebrow moved up skeptically. She pushed a clump of tangled hair from her eyes. It was one of her days off and she was still in her pyjamas, having slept late into the morning. —The combined effort of working days at Zelga's shop and studying her spell book late into the night was beginning to wear on her. And after yesterday's mad encounter she had been unable to get to sleep until deep into the night, long after Jenny had put out the light.

G alvanized with fascination, Heath's imagination devoured a hundred tantalizing possibilities which hung before her mind's eye all concerning the two dazzling sorceresses who had rescued her yesterday from... From what? Her *wind*? The wind from a past life? Heath did not know, and none of the brief explanations offered by the two women served to enlighten her a great deal. 'Later,' they told her, and like a pair of cats, they slipped away, vanishing into the cracks of the city as mysteriously as they had appeared.

"Later? How *much* later? I've got questions right *now!*"

Heath found it nearly impossible to sleep that night, and she awoke feeling groggy the next morning to the sound of Rubel rattling at her bedroom window. She pushed it open and caught her breath at the sight of the boy. He stood shining like a hero on the rooftop before her, sun glinting from the arsenal of golden weapons slung over his shoulder. Happy and triumphant, he greeted her beaming, and recounted with self loving zeal his adventures since he had last seen her. Heath was very nearly swept up into his blaze of charisma and personal aura for Rubel was in the *best* of spirits, but when Heath was feeling testy, (as she felt now,) she was not one to be swept anywhere.

After a while, Rubel frowned. "Well I don't know if they were leaving me alone with her on *purpose*. It just happened to work out that way a few times. What are you trying to say exactly?"

Heath huffed loudly. "That it's obviously a *trick!* They're trying to fool you into trusting her!"

"No! That's not it!" he cried, not even pausing to reflect. "How can you say that?"

"Because witches are sneaky and cruel that way... I bet they're trying to get you to fall in love with her."

"Sounds like it worked, if you ask me," Varkias put in, hopping to the window sill to watch the growing argument.

"Shut up, Varkias! I'm not in love with her! She's just... I don't know. I just like her." Rubel frowned.

"She's really pretty, I bet," Heath said, squinting at him.

Rubel said nothing.

"Grr! I knew it! How could you be so *stupid?*"

"Yeah! First the Shadow Lady, and now this." Varkias looked him up and down. "You sure are a big sucker for women!"

"No I'm not!" Rubel cried, exasperated. "I'm not a sucker for women!"

Heath and Varkias gazed at him skeptically.

"No! It's not like that! It's... The Shadow Lady is *good* inside. She wasn't tricking me!"

"Yes she was," Varkias said, getting exasperated himself. "She even *said* so."

"Yeah, but that's *different!* Argh! I was already arguing about this with Sara Blue!"

"And I bet she said to stay away from her," the imp cried. "The Shadow Lady admitted herself that she was tricking you into thinking she was crying and weak and needed your help. She said she would have even been *embarrassed* about acting that way if it hadn't worked so well!"

Heath goggled. "She actually *said* that?"

"Well, *yeah.*," Rubel admitted. "But, only because she's being *controlled*. She's got two halves, and one half is *good*! You guys don't know anything!"

Rubel nodded at their silence. "Exactly. And what if Kim turns out to really need my help? What then?" The imp and girl were again quiet. Heath's frown deepened as Rubel demanded, "Are you telling me I should just leave her there to get killed? I don't want to do that! And besides, she could be really useful. She probably knows all of Locumire's secrets, I bet. I know what I'm doing! You have to trust me on this stuff. I'm the one who's the thief around here!"

"Well. .," Heath faltered, looking a little ashamed. "It isn't like you've been telling us what's been going on all this time. You said you were going to meet me after school. You said you were going to find out if Jenny was a prostitute or not!"

"She's not."

Heath sat up. "What?"

"I followed her. She works in a customs office on the docks. She has a regular job."

Heath blinked. "Really?"

"Yeah."

"Oh. Gee… Well, that's a relief! —I mean, I didn't *really* think she was a prostitute. I knew she wasn't. But those kids at school got me all worried. Wow. I'm really glad you followed her! Thanks."

"Yeah. .," Rubel pondered. "But I still wonder why she wouldn't tell you where she worked. And it's such a weird story for kids to tell. Pirates and all. I wonder how it got started."

They were both quiet a moment before Heath's cheeks grew flushed and her eyes shot sparks.

"You changed the subject! You're still a thoughtless jerk!"

Rubel blinked. "What?"

"You just vanished! You said you were going to meet me, but you didn't show up for two whole days! Who do you think you are?! —You think you're so great you can just take off and not care about anybody but yourself?!"

Rubel looked at her aghast.

"I got locked in a coffin!" he protested. "I didn't *mean* to get caught! And anyway, I just escaped! I came straight here!"

"No you didn't! You went see those mermaids first!"

"More women," Varkias commented.

Rubel turned on him and threw up his arms, "They're FISH!" he cried. "And I needed weapons! So I went to them first. What difference does it make!?"

"*They* didn't think you were missing!" Heath complained. "*They* weren't all worried about you!"

Varkias folded his arms. "Yeah!"

Rubel paused.

"You guys were worried about me?"

"Duh! What do you *think?*" Heath rolled her eyes. "You think we *wouldn't* be worried?"

"I don't know... Wow. Gee. I sort of thought..." He looked at them a little sheepishly. "Well I just thought you didn't care so much about me. Now that you have each other, and all..."

Heath's eyes blazed.

"What?" She demanded. "How stupid could anybody be?! So THAT'S why you want to be friends with a *witch?* And with my crazy sister? Rubel! Why would you think we don't care? You're the only guy either of us know in this whole place! Heck, all my friends died a thousand years ago! I've got more reason to be lonely than you! And anyway, Varkias and me can't help being best friends again. We've been together in all my past lives. We've been best friends for thousands of years! WAY before *you* ever met him. You barely know him!"

Rubel looked sad and hurt at this, and Heath caught herself too late.

"Yeah, I know now," he said. "I just didn't realize it when I was a kid. I guess I just thought... I don't know."

"Erg." Heath bit her lip. "I'm sorry. I guess I can see what you're talking about. It would feel kind of bad to have your best friend switch over to somebody else..."

"Urg." Varkias wriggled uncomfortably. "Do we have to talk about this?"

They sat in silence, each mulling their thoughts and not looking at each other. After a time, Heath huffed to herself, recalling how she had met the king in the Dragon's Garden and how he had spoken when those about him were confused and in need of leadership. She took a deep breath and Rubel and Varkias both watched as she stood.

WOW. WE'RE THE REAL THING, AREN'T WE?

I THINK WE ARE.

AND WE ALREADY HAVE A TOUGH DECISION TO MAKE AS OUR FIRST TASK.

WE HAVE TO FIGURE OUT WHAT TO DO ABOUT THIS WITCH YOU MET.

KIM...

YEAH.

HM! -WE'RE FINALLY GETTING OUR TEAM TOGETHER, AND ALL THIS STUFF IS HAPPENING.

I DON'T LIKE IT.

I DON'T FEEL AS IF WE'RE READY.

OKAY, LOOK. HERE'S HOW IT'S ALL GOING TO GO. -KIM WILL WANT YOU TO FALL IN LOVE AND SWEAR YOURSELF TO HER.

WHATEVER YOU DO, DON'T.

THAT WOULD BE EXACTLY WHAT LOCUMIRE WANTS.

YEESH...

ALSO, DON'T TELL HER ABOUT ME OR GIVE AWAY ANY SECRETS. -NONE OF THE WITCHES KNOW I'M IN THE CITY YET AND WE HAVE TO KEEP IT THAT WAY.

RIGHT.

SECOND..,

IF SHE WANTS TO COME WITH YOU, WHATEVER YOU DO, DON'T BRING HER HERE OR TO ANY PLACE YOU WOULDN'T WANT LOCUMIRE TO KNOW ABOUT.

THAT MEANS SHE'LL HAVE TO FIGURE SOMETHING OUT ON HER OWN.

AFTER YOU BOTH ESCAPE, DON'T OFFER ANYTHING.
-LET HER MAKE ALL THE DECISIONS.
THAT WAY SHE MIGHT GIVE SOMETHING AWAY.

DO YOU HAVE ANYWHERE ELSE YOU COULD TAKE HER? AN OLD HIDEOUT OR SOMETHING?

HM. NOT REALLY. I USUALLY JUST SLEEP UNDER ROCKS AND IN TREES AND STUFF...

BUT WHAT IF SHE REALLY IS IN TROUBLE AND DOESN'T HAVE ANYWHERE TO GO? I'M SUPPOSED TO JUST LET HER SPEND THE NIGHT OUT IN THE STREETS GETTING COLD AND SCARED?

THAT'S NOT VERY HEROIC. WHAT KIND OF RESCUE IS THAT?

IT'S NOT ABOUT BEING A HERO!

THIS IS A SORCERER'S GAME.

YOU CAN'T JUST DO WHAT YOUR HEART WANTS.

YOU HAVE TO BE SMART.

LOOK, JUST TAKE HER TO AN INN, OR SOMETHING. —SHE'S RICH I BET, SO SHE'LL HAVE MONEY. LET HER SPEND A FEW DAYS THERE, AND WE'LL FIGURE OUT WHAT TO DO ABOUT HER LATER.

I GUESS I COULD TAKE HER SOMEPLACE OUTSIDE THE CITY WHERE IT'S SAFER.

I COULD STEAL A COUPLE OF HORSES...

GOOD. GOOO...

HMM...

WHAT?

THIS IS WEIRD.

—PLOTTING AGAINST LOCUMIRE.

I LEARNED A BIT ABOUT HER FROM A THOUSAND YEARS AGO WHEN QUINTON WAS FIGHTING AGAINST HER...

SHE WAS PRETTY SMART BACK THEN, AND SHE'LL HAVE LEARNED A LOT SINCE.

NO MATTER WHAT YOU DO, SHE'LL ALMOST CERTAINLY HAVE A WAY OF TURNING IT TO HER ADVANTAGE.

—I MEAN, IF YOU HADN'T ESCAPED FROM THE COFFIN, IT WOULD HAVE MEANT THAT YOU WEREN'T REALLY VERY TOUGH OR DANGEROUS.

—SHE'D HAVE JUST KILLED YOU OR KEPT YOU TO USE AGAINST THE SHADOW LADY. BUT WHEN YOU DID ESCAPE, SHE HAD A PRETTY GIRL THERE FOR YOU TO FALL IN LOVE WITH, SO SHE COULD CONTROL YOU THAT WAY...

I'M JUST WORRIED THAT IF THINGS DON'T GO IN A WAY THAT SHE PREDICTED...

WELL..,

THAT WITCH IN QUINTON'S TOWER DIDN'T SEEM TO HAVE MUCH TROUBLE KNOCKING YOU FLAT.

MAGIC IS BAD FOR THIEVES. IT'S YOUR WEAK SPOT.

BUT I HAVE MERMAID WEAPONS THIS TIME...

THEY MAY NOT BE ENOUGH.

HM!

HERE, LET ME SEE THAT AMULET THEY GAVE YOU.

HM...

UM, SURE... HOLD ON.

ERK!

I TRIED IT ON BEFORE I CAME HERE.

I CAN HARDLY WALK WHEN I PUT IT ON!

AND THINGS I'M CARRYING ALL TRY TO POINT IN THE SAME DIRECTION.

IT'S VERY AWKWARD.

I'M A LITTLE WORRIED BECAUSE I PROMISED LAUROL I'D WEAR IT.

YOU KNOW THAT THING?

—FROM A PAST LIFE MAYBE?

SHH.

LET ME USE YOUR KNIFE.

UH, SURE.

HEY! I HAVE TO GIVE THAT BACK...

POP

OKAY.

I THINK THIS THING MIGHT BE USEFUL.

I'M PRETTY SURE IT WAS MADE TO DEFLECT MORE THAN JUST KNIVES AND ARROWS.

—I POPPED OFF THE BROWN GEM AND THE GREEN GEM.

—BROWN MEANS EARTH THINGS, LIKE METAL AND ROCKS, AND GREEN IS LIFE, WHICH MEANS THINGS LIKE FISTS AND WOOD AND YOUR OWN ARMS AND LEGS.

I WAS READING ABOUT THIS IN TRISHA'S BOOK.

THE GEMS ARE SET IN A LINE, AND THE DESIGN IN THE SILVER IS VERY ROUGH, SO IT'S A PRETTY SIMPLE AMULET.

SINCE THEY WEREN'T SET IN A PATTERN, TAKING TWO OF THEM OUT WON'T AFFECT HOW THE OTHERS WORK.

I DON'T THINK.

SO NOW IT WON'T STOP SWORDS, BUT IT WON'T MAKE YOUR LEGS OR ARMS GO STIFF, EITHER.

BUT THESE OTHER GEMS...

I DON'T KNOW WHAT THEY ALL MEAN, BUT THOSE PURPLE ONES I THINK HAVE TO DO WITH SPIRIT.

LOCUMIRE'S PALACE WILL BE SURROUNDED BY SPELLS WHICH WILL LET THEM KNOW WHEN YOU ENTER.

BUT IF YOU WEAR THAT, I THINK IT SHOULD MAKE IT SO YOU CAN GO IN AND NOT GET NOTICED.

HEY..! THAT'S PRETTY GOOD!

YOU ARE GOOD AT THIS STUFF!

WELL, IT WON'T MAKE YOU INVISIBLE, SO YOU STILL HAVE TO BE CAREFUL.

HE-EATH! IT'S TIME TO START GETTING READY. COME BACK IN, PLEASE!

Vale made a quiet clucking sound as she surveyed Jenny's handiwork; the hair braids and the starchy white dress she had put Heath into. Heath shuffled uncomfortably beneath the woman's gaze and wished that Jenny had not left the pair of them alone together.

"Hmm," Vale pursed her lips and shook her head. "If it wasn't for that large forehead of yours. . . And those elbows. So pointy and bony. But then, I suppose this is the best we can really expect, isn't it? That dress certainly made Islen look pretty when *she* wore it." She remarked this in a way which managed to be both critical and dismissive in the same tone. She sighed, affecting an attitude of theatrical perseverance, and stepped back into the shafts of late afternoon sunlight so that they illuminated her own perfect evening gown in hues of yellow and gold. "But you must understand, we're not about to waste what little money Jenny brings home to calm your petty worries; trying in vain to fix up your looks is quite hopeless. Please try not to be so selfish about it."

Selfish. . ?! Heath's heart flared with rage for an instant. She had never until that moment considered her forehead or elbows to be anything more or less than a forehead and elbows, and though she knew it was just another of Vale's pecks at her self confidence, before Heath could catch herself, she ran a finger over one elbow only to find that it *did* feel pointy. Vale noticed this and nodded sagely, and Heath almost exploded with fury. Thus she stood fuming and itching in the old, expensive dress which had once belonged to a girl about her size; Jenny's real daughter. And Vale's granddaughter. Heath made a fierce effort to regain her self resolution before the sickly air of Vale's unending dislike for her. "I bring in money too," she growled just over her breath. "A lot more than *you* do!"

V ale rose dangerously. "Pardon me?" she demanded, standing regal and tall above the girl. Social events were *her* territory and she was already drawing power from the early evening. "Are you suggesting that we ought to provide you with food and shelter *and* clothing out of our own pocket? —That you should not have to lift a finger to earn our generosity? Is that what you think?"

Heath, her head seething with hot emotions, could not think of a good answer to this. "No. .," she faltered. "I don't think *that. . ."* Vale gazed down at her imperiously, and Heath, grinding her teeth, was only able to force herself turn her head up enough so that she could glare back darkly from beneath the blurring ridge of her eyebrows.

"Quite. I should hope not! I trust that's settled then." Vale regarded her for a long moment more before going on. "Yes. . . In the future you would do well to brush your hair forward to cover that prominent forehead of yours. I am suggesting this only because it's fair that somebody should let you know. Most people are too squeamish to offer a person the necessary advice they need to hear. —Ah, Jennifer. There you are."

"The roast is nearly done," Jenny said, stepping into Heath's room. "Evelene is just putting it out to warm." She hesitated, looking down at Heath whose cheeks were red and whose eyes were blazing. "Is everything all right?"

"Yes, yes," Vale said quickly. "But I'm glad you're here. Please sit down. There is a matter I want to discuss with you both before the guests start to arrive." A curious note entered her voice. "It is something you have both been avoiding, but I feel it is time to make some matters clear."

Jenny stiffened as she sat down beside Heath on the bed spread. Heath, still boiling from indignation felt her gut scrunch up even tighter.

have been telling people," she began, "that Heath will only be staying with us for another three days. That she'll be going home to her parents. I've told people that word came yesterday about her mother and how she is making excellent progress in recovering from the 'sickness' she contracted, and that the doctors are quite relieved. I'm doing nothing wrong in this; I'm only building on the lie I've been told. —By both of you." She bore her eyes into Jenny's, and Heath felt the blood leave her lips. "I happen to know that none of it is true at all, but it's what I've been told and so it's what I've been telling. Mr. Perkin has made it explicit that he does not want to be inheriting somebody else's children and responsibilities by marrying you, Jenny."

"You mean his *father* has made it explicit! I am *not* marrying Geof Perkin! The man is a spineless worm! And," she raised her finger before her mother could interrupt her, "And Heath is *not* going to be going home. She has no home to go back *to.* This has been quite clear from the beginning."

"Perhaps you ought to have considered that when you misreported her to the prince's duty men," Vale said menacingly. "Telling lies to the authorities is no small matter, Jennifer! There's no knowing how much trouble you could get us all into. One lie leads to another. —I've had to be *most* creative when people ask for more details! And father or son, Mr. Perkin will not marry you unless *she* goes. *That* is quite final. She must pack her things and be gone before the wedding."

"Wedding!? Mother! There is not going to *be* a wedding!" Jenny stood, a fire now alight in her own eyes. "And just *where* is Heath supposed to go?"

"That is no interest of mine," Vale replied archly. "She'll just have to find another family to intrude upon. If nothing else, she clearly has an aptitude for *that*!"

Heath's mouth went dry. She'd had no idea this had been brewing. —Or rather, she *had*. She'd seen it every day plain upon Vale's face; she'd seen it on the walls and in the air of the living room which was Vale's den and throne chamber.

To begin with, after Heath had first moved in, she believed that Vale might simply sit in her rocking chair and fume and cluck and do nothing more, that her bitterness would remain an immovable mountain whose frosty peaks would never change and never thaw. And that is certainly how it had been, but Heath now vaguely recalled that mountains sometimes also exploded.

Jenny began to flush with anger.

"I will not have this, Mother! If you persist. . ."

Vale looked down at her daughter, her face set with a stale calm. "Yes. . ?"

Jenny blustered. "Well, I may decide to tell everybody about my father. My *real* father!"

A wincing silence fell upon the room, and Heath knew at once that Jenny had used some hidden power which she had been saving for just such a moment as this. Except something was wrong. . .

Vale did not flinch. Indeed, the old woman took on an expression which seemed to say, *'Ah. But you see, I am ready for you!'* A horrible draft passed through Heath as Vale luxuriated in her bitter moment. Jenny's eyes registered confusion.

"I am shocked that you would ever suggest such a thing," Vale said darkly. "You would disgrace your own *mother?* Your mother, who loves you above all else?"

"It is only because I care for her," Jenny faltered. "Heath is good and brave. It is wrong to drive her away!"

Vale stalked from one end of the room to the other, her evening gown moving like a crisp phantom. Heath and Jenny both watched her in fearful, absolute attention.

You and the girl should know then, if this is how you wish to be. . , it has come to my attention that some parties would be very interested in learning that a girl named *Wingwhit* is here in the city."

Heath caught her breath and her heart went cold as Vale's eyes pierced savagely into her. Jenny stood up in fury.

"Mother! You would not! *You must not!* If you turn her in, I'd never forgive you! Mother, you *absolutely must not!*"

"And I won't. If you do as I say. If she leaves. —I'll be fair. I've no desire to be anything but fair. I've given this a great deal of thought. We'll give her three days more to get her affairs straightened away, but then after that, she goes."

"Three days?" Jenny cried. "Mother! *She's just a child!"*

"Oh, I think she is somewhat more than just a child. *She* knows what she is!" Vale said, stabbing her chin at Heath, her voice filled with venom. "And if she is not gone three days from this very moment, I will turn her in myself!"

"But I never did anything wrong!" Heath gasped in helpless protest, a thousand images of orphanages and of homes which were not her own flashing through her mind's eye; thoughts she had begun to truly believe she had finally left behind her. Jennifer cast about desperately.

"Then. . . Then, perhaps Zelga would. . ."

Her mother shook her head.

"No. She must leave the city. To stay behind and live under somebody else's care would make us look cruel. It would mean that her mother has not recovered and that we are forcing her to leave against her will. You must stick to the story you created for yourselves. That is quite beyond my control."

"But *mother. . !"*

"You'll do as I say, or I'll turn her over to the prince's authorities. I should think she would *want* to leave the city to get away from her enemies! Sticking your head in the sand is foolish. Nobody can hope to live in a fantasy for very long."

Vale moved towards the door. "Now all of that is final. I expect you'll want to cry and rage about up here for a while, and that's fine. I've allowed some time for this. But be sure, Jenny, that your make-up is fresh and that you do not come downstairs looking at all flustered when the guests start to arrive. And be particularly pleasant to Geof Perkin. He will be asking for your hand in marriage tonight, and I have assured him that you will be happy to accept."

Jenny's mouth fell open in horror, but she could make no words come forth.

"And if you fail to accept his offer. .," her mother warned. "If you embarrass me, then I will turn the girl over to the authorities this very evening!"

"Mother. . !" Tears welled up in Jenny's eyes. "*Mom!* Please!"

Vale ignored her, and paused to look over Heath one more time. "Hm. . . And *do* try not to spill anything on yourself as you did the other night with the gravy boat. Try to remember that those clothes do not belong to you. I'd just as soon leave you up here all evening, but the guests are curious to see you and it would seem odd if you were not to make an appearance." With that, she turned and left the room.

WOW, EVERYTHING'S GONE. -EVEN THE COFFIN!

RATS! THAT'S WHERE I LEFT MY OTHER BOOT.

I WAS HOPING TO FIND IT.

IT GETS UNCOMFORTABLE GOING AROUND WITH ONE LEG TALLER THAN THE OTHER.

I'D BETTER GO BAREFOOT.

≥ SIGH. ≤
MY GRANDFATHER MADE THESE FOR ME HIMSELF...

IT'S NO BIG DEAL. I GO BAREFOOT ALL THE TIME.

WE HAVE TO BE CAREFUL, VARKIAS.

I'VE NEVER DEALT WITH WITCHES ON PURPOSE BEFORE. THIS IS NEW FOR ME.

YEAH... HAVE YOU GOT THAT AMULET HEATH FIXED FOR YOU?

YES.

OKAY. I'M READY. LET'S GO.

Wholesome cooking smells which had been brewing all day were now filling the house from bottom to top, and it wasn't very long before the cheery, clunking sounds of guests making their arrivals began to drift up from downstairs. As Vale had predicted, Heath and Jenny did cry, and Jenny, aware that Heath was the child and that she was the adult, made an effort to assure that everything would right itself; that they'd figure *something* out. But both of them knew she was just saying this and that the world was really a cruel and unfair place, and that their love for one another simply wasn't going to be enough today, and so they held each other tightly as they cried.

Downstairs, the guests continued to arrive and make their cheery sounds, and in her heart, Heath knew that her world was changing again, forever and intractably. She could feel it in her bones.

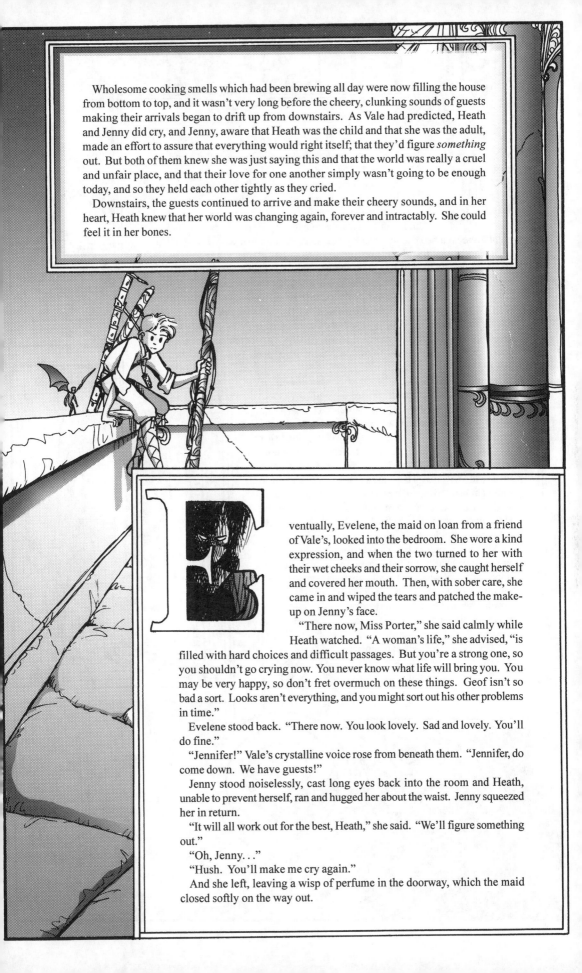

E ventually, Evelene, the maid on loan from a friend of Vale's, looked into the bedroom. She wore a kind expression, and when the two turned to her with their wet cheeks and their sorrow, she caught herself and covered her mouth. Then, with sober care, she came in and wiped the tears and patched the make-up on Jenny's face.

"There now, Miss Porter," she said calmly while Heath watched. "A woman's life," she advised, "is filled with hard choices and difficult passages. But you're a strong one, so you shouldn't go crying now. You never know what life will bring you. You may be very happy, so don't fret overmuch on these things. Geof isn't so bad a sort. Looks aren't everything, and you might sort out his other problems in time."

Evelene stood back. "There now. You look lovely. Sad and lovely. You'll do fine."

"Jennifer!" Vale's crystalline voice rose from beneath them. "Jennifer, do come down. We have guests!"

Jenny stood noiselessly, cast long eyes back into the room and Heath, unable to prevent herself, ran and hugged her about the waist. Jenny squeezed her in return.

"It will all work out for the best, Heath," she said. "We'll figure something out."

"Oh, Jenny..."

"Hush. You'll make me cry again."

And she left, leaving a wisp of perfume in the doorway, which the maid closed softly on the way out.

Heath sat back on the corner of the bed to cast her gaze longingly through the window and into the dusky summer night beyond. The room was filled with sadness, and beneath that, a warm, surreal sense seemed to float. It spread through Heath's entire being, warming her, lifting her. She pressed herself to the glass, feeling the cool panes against her cheek and then flinging the window open, leaned far out into the night. She breathed deeply upon the heat thickened air and wished with all her heart that she could escape into it. And soon she would! There was *never* anything stable for her in life. She had been stupid to hope for it. To attempt it! It flew in the face of nature. The realization of this touched her for the first time as though it were a heavenly truth, and she laughed at it. For half an instant her heart rushed with a wild longing to leap from the window and fly. She was giddy, soaring with this feeling for a moment, before it calmed and mingled with the sound of falsetto greetings of more people arriving. She watched the tops of their heads at the front door below her as the light from inside illuminated their bodies in amber and yellow.

After a while, the maid returned to fetch her downstairs to meet the guests. Heath descended the stairs in a cloud, dreamily imagining that she might say clever things which would really be veiled remarks designed to cut and make Vale look as foul as she was. The floaty feeling made her laugh at these thoughts, but when she reached the bottom of the stairs, she discovered that many of the guests seemed already to know her. They gazed at her archly and made quiet comments to themselves out of her hearing. To them, all she managed to say were things which fell quite flat and sounded quite stupid. "*Vale's* friends," she thought sickly as the world began to grow heavy again.

After her presence had passed from the attention of introductions, she managed to slip away from the pre-dinner talk. She wandered aimlessly from one end of the house to the other, until at last feeling hot and crowded, she let herself outside to the steps where she plopped down like a deflated balloon.

"This is terrible!" she exclaimed to nobody.

The night said nothing back.

Chapter 9

LEHANNA..?

SHUT UP!

LOCUMIRE AND SASHAH WILL BE HERE SOON.

THERE'S HARDLY ANY TIME.

-KIM! I KNOW WHAT YOU'RE PLANNING TO DO.

I KNOW YOU'RE PLANNING TO RUN AWAY WITH THAT BOY FOR REAL.

ULP..! LEA-

WHAT? YOU THINK I'M STUPID?

YOU THINK LOCUMIRE IS STUPID?

I BET SHE ALREADY KNOWS!

I BET SHE EVEN HAS A PLAN IN CASE THIS HAPPENED!

SHE'S TOO OLD AND TOO SMART, KIM.

YOU CAN'T DEFY HER!

HMP!

LOCUMIRE'S NOT SO TOUGH.

WE'RE STRONGER THAN NEARLY ALL THE GIRLS HERE. -I WAS READING ABOUT IT.

IN OUR PAST LIVES, WE USED TO BE SORCERER-EMPRESSES BEFORE LOCUMIRE WAS EVEN BORN!

WHAT?

WHAT ARE YOU TALKING ABOUT?

I'M SERIOUS.

GOING WAY BACK.

OUR PAST LIVES HAVE BEEN CIRCLING AROUND THE GREAT LORD ALMOST FOREVER. -WE WERE EVEN SORACIA'S MOST TRUSTED SERVANTS ONCE.

WHAT ARE YOU TALKING ABOUT?

ARE YOU KIDDING?

NO, REALLY! WE'RE REALLY IMPORTANT.

I KNOW THINGS, KIM. LOCUMIRE HAS BEEN TELLING ME SECRETS THAT YOU DON'T KNOW ABOUT.

IT'S BECAUSE SHE THINKS YOU'RE NOT FOCUSED ENOUGH IN YOUR THINKING. YOU'RE NOT FIXED ENOUGH IN YOUR BELIEFS.

YOU DON'T KNOW WHAT YOU WANT, AND THAT'S WHY SHE LEFT YOU OUT OF THE INNER CIRCLE.

INNER CIRCLE? HA! I KNOW ALL ABOUT THAT, AND I DON'T WANT IT.

I KNOW WHAT I WANT.

I WANT TO BE AWAY FROM ALL THIS!

IT'S LIKE SORACIA LADY WAS SAYING. THERE'S SOMETHING WRONG HERE, LEAHANNA.

I'M SICK OF ALL THE PARTIES AND THE WINE AND THE BLACK MAGIC. ALL THIS SUPERFICIAL CRAP!

NOBODY'S FOR REAL HERE.

IT'S ALL ETIQUETTE AND POWER GAMING, AND EVERYBODY IS SCARED OF EVERYBODY ELSE.

PEOPLE DIE HERE, LEA!

IT'S LIKE I'M STUCK IN SOME KIND OF PRETEND DREAM WITH NO FRIENDS.

WHERE ALL MY FRIENDS ARE SHADOWS.

I'M NOT A SHADOW..!

WELL THAT'S WHAT IT FEELS LIKE THESE DAYS!

EXCEPT THERE'S A WAY OUT AND SORACIA SAW IT, AND SHE'S NOT SCARED TO HUNT AFTER IT.

LOCUMIRE SEES IT TOO, BUT SHE IS SCARED.

SCARED TO LEAVE THIS...

THIS ROTTEN POWER DREAM BEHIND.

HEATH
IS
PROTECTED.

BOM

Chapter 10

HI... I DIDN'T KNOW YOU WERE INVITED.

GEOF?

HA! HA!

WHATEVER POSSESSED **YOU** TO SHOW UP, ROBINS?

DON'T TELL ME VALE HAD **YOU** INVITED?!

NO. I DIDN'T EVEN KNOW THERE WAS EVEN SOMETHING HAPPENING TONIGHT.

I JUST CAME BY TO SEE JENNY.

NO WAY! HE CAME TO **CALL** ON HER..!

HA! HA! I DON'T BELIEVE THIS GUY!

HOW PATHETIC!

DON'T YOU THINK IF YOU EVER STOOD A CHANCE WITH HER, SHE MIGHT HAVE **INVITED** YOU?

DON'T WASTE YOUR TIME. —GO BACK TO THE BARRACKS WHERE YOU BELONG!

PARDON ME?!

WHAT ARE YOU TALKING ABOUT?!

USE YOUR BRAIN, FOOL!

IF YOU MUST KNOW, MISS PORTER IS TO BE ENGAGED TO OUR BROTHER THIS EVENING.

ENGAGED?!

TO GEOF?!

YOU CAN'T BE SERIOUS!

YOU THINK YOURSELF BETTER?

PHAW!

— GRANTED, JENNY'S NO PRIZE, BUT THERE'S AT LEAST A LITTLE BIT OF BLOOD IN HER. THAT'S MORE THAN A MILKSOP LIKE YOU CAN CLAIM!

GO ON DOWN TO THE DOCKS AND FIND SOME TROLLOP MORE SUITED TO YOUR SORT!

ARE YOU LOOKING FOR A FIGHT, SIR!?

AND SCUFF ABOUT WITH YOU?

DON'T JOKE WITH ME!

REST ASSURED!

I'D RUN YOU THROUGH IF YOU WERE WORTH THE EFFORT, BUT REST ASSURED, I WOULDN'T WASTE MY TIME!

I WOULDN'T WASTE MY TIME!

GET LOST, ROBINS.

THREATENING PROMINENT CITIZENS? —PERHAPS WE OUGHT TO TALK TO YOUR COMMANDING OFFICER.

TUCKER SPENCE, ISN'T IT?

HE'S NO FAN OF YOURS!

PERHAPS I WAS MOVING TOO SLOWLY...

BUT I DIDN'T WANT TO MAKE ANY...

ARGH..!

WHAT AM I TO DO? THIS CAN'T BE HAPPENING!

I MUST SEE HER!

VALE WON'T LET YOU IN. —SHE'S TERRIBLE.

I THINK SHE MIGHT EVEN BE EVIL!

I KNOW.

THEN I'LL BURST IN! I MUST SEE HER AT ONCE!

LOOK AT THAT BOY!

THAT BOY MEANS TROUBLE.

I'D RATHER IF NOBODY KNEW HE WAS EVEN OUT THERE.

TAKE BEFFEN AND SEND HIM ON HIS WAY.

BE CAUTIOUS!

DON'T LET HIM DRAW. —HE'S A BETTER SWORDS-MAN THAN EITHER OF YOU. —NO BLOOD TONIGHT, YOU HEAR?

HRM..! WHATEVER YOU SAY, DAD.

THIS IS FOUL!

MEN WILL DIE TONIGHT!

WHAT? NO! THEY'LL KILL YOU!

HM! WE'LL SEE ABOUT THAT!

NO! —EVEN IF YOU WIN, THE PRINCE WILL EXECUTE YOU!

AND THEN THERE WON'T BE ANY CHANCE AT ALL FOR YOU AND JENNY!

YOU'RE NO GOOD TO ANYBODY IF YOU'RE DEAD!

IT WAS JENNY'S MOTHER WHO SET THIS ALL UP! —THERE'S JUST NOT ENOUGH MONEY, SO SHE WANTS JENNY TO MARRY SOMEBODY RICH.

IF YOU GET KILLED, IT'LL BE PLAYING INTO HER HANDS.

SO DON'T DO IT!

THEN I SUPPOSE THIS IS WHAT ZELGA WANTED ME TO SEE!

MRS. ZELGA SENT YOU?

SHE SEEMED TO THINK YOU BOTH MIGHT BE IN TROUBLE.

HM. TROUBLE INDEED!

I DON'T KNOW HOW, BUT I THINK ZELGA MUST KNOW ABOUT ME.

ARGH! THIS IS RIDICULOUS!

—I'M BOUND, BUT I CANNOT LET THIS HAPPEN!

GOOD!

GOOD LUCK!

SAME TO YOU!

GIRL!!

WHAT ARE YOU DOING OUT HERE?!

WHAT WAS HE SAYING TO YOU?

NOTHING!

IT'S NONE OF YOUR BUSINESS!

HMM...

DINNER IS BEING SERVED.

COME INSIDE.

SHOOK

WHA~?

he swirls of blue glaze around the rim of the plate were the same as those decorating the salt shaker. They were obviously pieces to the same set. Heath absently placed the salt shaker on the table and gazed into the plate before her. The blue ocean swirls were fantastically rich in both pattern and color, and staring, they absorbed her attention entirely so that she could not tear her eyes away. The patterns seemed almost to move.

She squinted into the shapes; ships and waves and seagulls. The glossy white of the plate's belly shone and flashed, clasping at her attention, drawing her further in so that the clink of glasses and adult laughter faded from her ears leaving her somewhere else. Somewhere very far away. . .

Somewhere *older*. . .

Or rather. . .
Where *she* was older.
It smelled of the *Ocean*. . .

The party swam and was gone.

ove is a spectacular thing," Calypso advised thoughtfully in the afternoon light beneath the rasenut tree which overlooked the water. "But it is not something to be underestimated."

"Don't I know it!" Heath laughed. She felt tired, her muscles luxuriating under the languid embrace of that summer heat. She felt as though she might never move again, and breathed the fresh, salty air with her eyes closed. A fragment from a distant memory tugged at her mind and she frowned; A dining table with clinking glasses and adult laughter from long ago. . . Her head felt light, swimming. After a moment she shook the odd feeling.

Calypso remained serious. "Love is integral to life, Heath. It is one of the great engines in the world of mortals. But it is not an uncommon end. It has the power to drain away all that is special about you. It won't have been the first time you have chosen that path. But it would be curious, especially now, if you were to follow it again."

eath was put out by this. Thoughtful. But her bold, romantic dreams would not diminish in their demand to be paid their attention. As the months drifted by, all the mysterious powers of the world gathered to her side, rallying. The lantern party lights; the very stars dancing highlights in her hair, and her yellow dress lending magic which made her the rushing center of whatever scene she passed through. She danced with strange power and sparking eyes, capturing easily that elusive mood of primal danger which appealed to her. Old people sitting along the benches with hot drinks and memories, sighed and laughed at her youth while suitors watched in an agony of adoration. She was breathtaking. It was on such a night of summer festivities that Soracia melted from the shadows, her voice mellow with dark notes.

ister. Come away with me for a spell. I would talk with you."

"Ha! Come to the Rows with *me.* Come to the festival!" Heath said back, turning on her heel from the other young people she was with. "You would be marvelous. Like the old parties you boast to me about. —Casting your spell on a thousand people!" she laughed, challenging, holding her chin forward with defiance. She felt, however, Soracia's unearthly power, cool and sublime, curling across the stones, chilling her feet. Despite the pangs of deep pride and affection she felt for her sister, Heath had never entirely lost her fear. The gulf of time between them was just too great; like the Moon to the Earth. Soracia smiled and placed an ice hand upon Heath's shoulder so that the girl shuddered. The night hummed to the tidal force of Soracia's power.

"Cut that out," Heath said vaguely, awed with both fear and love. She shook her head with irritation. "What do you want?"

Soracia frowned, disapproveing. "We must speak on old matters. I will come to you again at midnight."

With that she slid away, back into the darkness and was gone. Heath shook her head again and huffed to herself with annoyance. The young men and women in their bright clothes called to her from the corner. "Coming!" she barked, and ran unashamedly to catch up. She moved with unconscious grace, back into that timeless dream of fragrant summer air, of her own vitality amidst the music and the glow of paper lanterns.

he evening passed quickly, and it was midnight sooner than she would have liked. She stole away from the festivities and found herself alone in a city hedge garden filled with evening flowers and ivy crawlers.

The Shadow Lady rose before her. "Well?" Heath asked. "I'm here." The trees whispered and dry leaves rattled quietly on the ground. Soracia was a fearful sight, but a strange memory of strength and magic was living in Heath that night and she did not waver.

Soracia smiled fondly at her, but her expression became serious. "Do you recall the boy thief?" she asked. "How much of you remains? . . . or are you leaving me entirely?"

"Boy thief?"

"A shaft of sunlight and a breath of wind. He was your close friend. You and he together were a force to contend with."

"What on earth are you talking about?" Heath frowned and shifted her weight from one foot to the other. "Sally?"

Her sister regarded her until Heath's gaze faltered.

"Well, he has returned."

"Who has?"

"Heath. . ." Soracia began and stopped, choosing her words. "The others say you must be allowed to move in your own course, and that we must follow without question. —That your wisdom is pure. Except I think otherwise. I know your true soul, and I think you have gotten lost as well. This is not you. You were always such a stubborn little realist! But they won't touch you because of what happened to Katara. They say that to influence you would lead to disaster. —But I have seen disaster. I have *been* disaster. . ." She gazed down, her face hard, filled with difficult thoughts none but she could see or understand. She looked up sharply. "They don't realize it, but they have become entranced as well. They were too confident in their own age and wisdom, and they watched you with pride. They drank your fragrance in like first wine, and it overtook them without their ever noticing. Your power flows over us all, and now only I remain. I am the last one who sees the world as it was. Even the Forest. . ." Her jaw was hard, but she looked up again with a softness in her eyes, a need which tempered the iron. "And I am far too selfish."

Heath felt a lump growing in her chest, believing that important matters were indeed at hand and that she had somehow not performed as she should have. She felt hunted and guilty, but she did not know why. "What are you talking about?" she repeated, but her voice wavered.

"They love Rubel. They were overjoyed to see him return, but at the same time they were afraid. . . Rubel can also see. He can see as I can. And he was *angry*, and they know he won't stay away from you. And he won't. Not unless I insist. My influence is the only one he obeys entirely now. He is a young man now. A wolf. His power is. . . immense. And he wants to end it as he thinks it should, in battle and blood. He despises dreams and lies. That is partly my doing. . . He will have it no other way but to cross swords at last. But he listens to me. I am the last chance."

Heath nodded, but understanding only Soracia's influence, not her words. Soracia was her only true anchor these days to something only half remembered. The only one she would bend for. But the rest of it caused her stomach to quiver. The warm, fragrant night receded from her limbs, leaving her cold.

"But I don't understand," she breathed, the lump in her chest growing.

"Everything is going to change, sister."

"But why. . ?"

"Because I love you both. . . Far too much. And Rubel will not be able to fight you. You know him too well, and you are too strong. He will only make you run and clasp to your dreams more tightly. You would eventually even suffocate me. Erase me. You are strong enough to do that, I think. So you must not hide anymore! You must wake up, and you must do it very soon. Choosing to stay with Jenny was a mistake. It was not meant to last as long as you forced it. Years. . !"

"No!" Heath's heart stabbed and though her confusion only grew, she knew it was true. She staggered backwards. "I don't understand!"

Soracia moved over the stones, her new cloak flowing like smoke and satin. She raised a pale arm and caressed her sister's cheek. ., pressed her palm to the girl's forehead. . .

"Oh, Heath. You were always so. . . Do you remember how we stopped fighting that once, long ago. Back when we were both *new*."

Heath stared, her thoughts distant and foggy.

"In the harvest," Soracia said, "without our parents, and there were all those other children from poor families. We were not prepared for it. Their games were so rough, the boys trying to push one another over the bonfires. And I didn't know where you were for nearly a week, until I saw you coming the other way along a path. Do you remember? You were my enemy, and I hated you even then, but you looked so lonely and sad and homesick, and I recognized immediately those same feelings within myself. You saw me and said, 'Hi,' but you broke down and cried and I hugged you. I'd never felt so lonely. Hugging you was like the opposite of dying, and I loved you so much right then. Do you remember that? All the stupid pretensions were put away for that moment."

Heath had tears in her eyes, and she nodded.

"Long, long ago." Soracia took her sister's face in both hands and gazed into Heath's eyes. "Heath, you must release the world. Let go. If you hold us here, I don't know what will happen, but I know I will fade away. The others don't even understand what you are doing, but I will be gone, and I don't want to leave. Not after coming so *far. . .*"

"I..."

A hand came down upon her shoulder, and Heath gasped as though she had been holding her breath. She choked, knocking some left over bones and potatoes onto the tablecloth from her plate. (She had eaten a whole meal!) Staggered with confusion, she tried to stand, almost tipping over backwards in her chair and Varkias, who had been pulling her hair to be noticed launched toward the ceiling in a craze of wings.

"Get off her, you crazy old hag! What have you done to her?!"

"Calm, child! You must breathe."

Heath's eyes whirled around, grasping for bearings, her head was hot and light.

Jenny, in her black evening gown, looked over in concern, and the adult laughter and conversation paused. Vale held Heath as the girl gasped for air.

"She's just choked, but she'll be fine. She's probably a little sick, I imagine, from sipping wine. I'll take her up to her room and open the window for some air. —No, no. Jenny, you stay with your guests. I've got her. She's just a little faint feeling. Come along, child."

Jenny hesitated, but Heath was too disoriented to send a desperate message with her expression, and Jenny as well seemed entranced in a way. Thus their last opportunity was missed. Vale however was quick and sharp and whisked Heath upstairs before another thing could happen.

"So you are a witch!" Vale declared fiercely, flinging the girl against a wall the instant Heath's bedroom door was shut and locked.

"What?" Heath gasped weakly.

"You had a *vision*. In the glaze. In the dishes," she said. "The plates are charmed. My sister sent them from the Fan Islands!"

Heath said nothing, her head still light. Varkias stayed to one side, saying nothing, casting his anxious expression back and forth between the two. Heath turned to face her.

"What happened to me?"

"A vision. You had a vision." Vale's face soured. "You are a *witch* at heart, child. Only a witch can have visions! I saw it in you from the first day you came here."

At this, a powerful surge rose through Heath and she realized all at once everything that was happening. "YOU CAST A SPELL ON ME!" she hollared in rage. "YOU CAST A SPELL ON ME SO I WOULDN'T BE ABLE TO TALK TO JENNY!! YOU'RE GOING TO MAKE HER MARRY THAT STUPID GEOF! YOU CAN'T! YOU *CAN'T!* SMITH ROBINS WILL STOP YOU! LET ME *GO!! OUCH!!"*

Vale yanked her wrists so violently that Heath's breath was snapped out of her again. Wrenching her arms together, Vale producing a cord which she had been carrying.

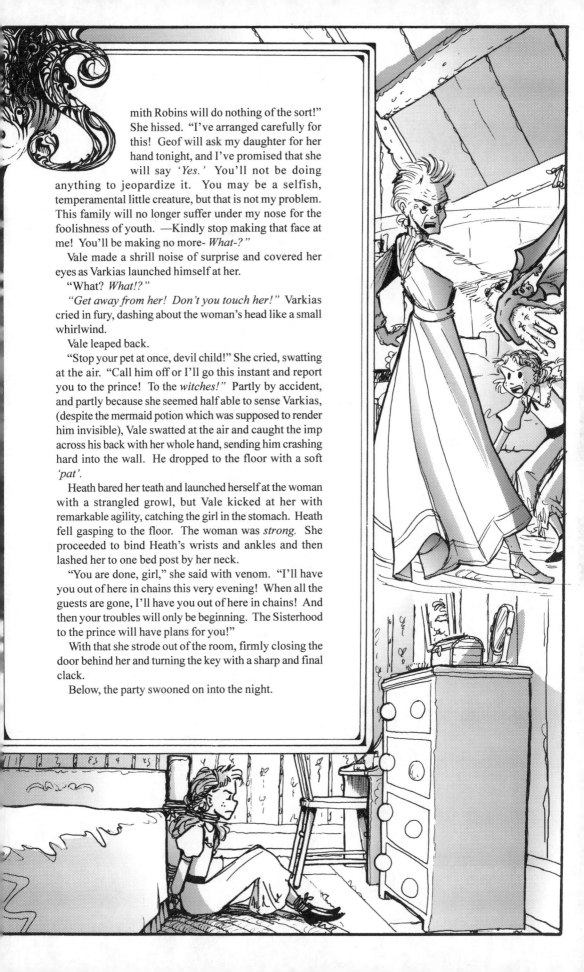

mith Robins will do nothing of the sort!"
She hissed. "I've arranged carefully for
this! Geof will ask my daughter for her
hand tonight, and I've promised that she
will say *'Yes.'* You'll not be doing
anything to jeopardize it. You may be a selfish,
temperamental little creature, but that is not my problem.
This family will no longer suffer under my nose for the
foolishness of youth. —Kindly stop making that face at
me! You'll be making no more- *What-?"*

Vale made a shrill noise of surprise and covered her
eyes as Varkias launched himself at her.

"What? *What!?"*

"Get away from her! Don't you touch her!" Varkias
cried in fury, dashing about the woman's head like a small
whirlwind.

Vale leaped back.

"Stop your pet at once, devil child!" She cried, swatting
at the air. "Call him off or I'll go this instant and report
you to the prince! To the *witches!"* Partly by accident,
and partly because she seemed half able to sense Varkias,
(despite the mermaid potion which was supposed to render
him invisible), Vale swatted at the air and caught the imp
across his back with her whole hand, sending him crashing
hard into the wall. He dropped to the floor with a soft
'pat'.

Heath bared her teeth and launched herself at the woman
with a strangled growl, but Vale kicked at her with
remarkable agility, catching the girl in the stomach. Heath
fell gasping to the floor. The woman was *strong*. She
proceeded to bind Heath's wrists and ankles and then
lashed her to one bed post by her neck.

"You are done, girl," she said with venom. "I'll have
you out of here in chains this very evening! When all the
guests are gone, I'll have you out of here in chains! And
then your troubles will only be beginning. The Sisterhood
to the prince will have plans for you!"

With that she strode out of the room, firmly closing the
door behind her and turning the key with a sharp and final
clack.

Below, the party swooned on into the night.

Chapter 11

YOU WERE BROUGHT HERE BECAUSE EACH ONE OF YOU IS A FAULTED MAN OF VIRTUE.

WHILE YOU HAVE BEEN IN THIS DREAM LAND, DARK THINGS HAVE FLOURISHED.

YOUR SHADOWS.

ON YOUR THRONES AND SEATS OF POWER SHADOWS HAVE RISEN; YOUR OPPOSITES AND YOUR EVILS FILL THE SPACES LEFT BEHIND IN THE WAKING WORLD.

YOUR BROTHER, ARMIS.

AND YOUR LONG TIME RIVAL, FULARO.

AND LORD RILLION...

MY SON.

YES.

HE IS BRILLIANT AND ANGRY. — NOT EVEN LOCUMIRE FULLY SUSPECTS...

HM...

INDEED.

THE DRAGON DREAMS SO FIERCELY OF EACH OF YOU THAT YOUR SHADOWS ARE CAST IN FULL BY THE LIGHT OF HIS MIND.

MOST PECULIAR.

DO YOU HAVE A SHADOW IN THE WAKING WORLD?

YES.

ONLY **RUBEL** WALKS WITHOUT A SHADOW. RUBEL IS MADE FROM THE SAME STUFF AS THE DRAGON I AM NOT. **I** HAVE A <u>SISTER</u>.

YOUR **DAUGHTER**. SHE IS BRIGHT AND BEAUTIFUL AND WITHOUT FLAW.

KATARA HAS SEEN BEYOND THE VEIL. —SHE MEANS TO CAST THE WORLD TO THE STARS.

HM...

WELL..., SHE DOES HAVE ONE FLAW, BUT IT IS NOT WITHIN HER.

THE YOUNG GIRL! —HEATH

ONE EMBODIES *POWER*

NAKED AND DEVASTATING.

A PATH I KNOW WELL.

IT WOULD BE SO *EASY*...

KATARA AND I COULD DIVIDE THE WORLD BETWEEN US IF...

WELL.

BUT HEATH.

HEATH IS SOMETHING *ELSE.*

SOMETHING ELSE ENTIRELY.

BAH! I CAN'T STAND THE WAYS OF YOU MAGICIANS!

YOUR WORDS TWIST UP IN MY EARS! —IT'S MADDENING.

HOW CAN A **SHADOW** BE A PERSON?!

BE WISE, GRINRUM.

IGNORE THE MACHINATIONS.

THEY ARE BEYOND MOST OF YOU.

I'VE HEARD TALK OF THIS KIND BEFORE.

LISTEN AND TREAD WITH CARE.

HRM!

I ONLY MENTION THEM TO GIVE MY WORDS SOME GROUNDING.

INDEEO!

I HAVE TRIED TO WAKEN MYSELF. I HAVE MEDITATED AND FOUGHT.

EACH MORNING I HOPE TO WAKE UP IN MY HOME, BUT NO...

HA! HA!

MMM...

JUST KNOWING THAT THIS PLACE IS A DREAM IS NOT ENOUGH.

—EVEN WITH THE STUPENDOUS ADVANTAGE OF HAVING EXPERIENCED BOTH THIS WORLD AND THE ONES YOU CAME FROM, YOU MUST HAVE GREATER FAITH THAN INTELLECT ALONE ALLOWS.

BELIEVE ME. YOURS IS NOT A UNIQUE BATTLE.

AMONG TRUE SORCERERS, IT IS THE ONLY BATTLE.

PAST NOON!

BUT NONE OF YOU NEED TO WORRY.

MOST OF YOU HAVE ALREADY DIED IN THE WAKING WORLD. —YOUR PASSAGE FROM HERE WILL BE A VERY SIMPLE MATTER.

WHAT?

EXCUSE ME?

I SLEW EACH OF YOU SHORTLY AFTER YOU WERE POISONED WITH DRAGON'S THE BLOOD.

I CAME TO EACH OF YOU IN YOUR TIMES, AND PLUNGED A SWORD INTO YOUR HEARTS.

WE HAVE DIED?

IT WAS A THREE-THOUSAND YEAR TASK; BUT IT WAS DONE. —YOU ARE ALL QUITE DEAD.

I SEE.

HM.

ALL EXCEPT FOR YOU TWO.

ARMIS, RILLION.

RILLION, YOU IN PARTICULAR.

YOU ARE THE MOST RECENT CAPTIVE HERE.

I HAD EMERGED INTO A DIFFERENT STATE OF MIND BY THE TIME I WAS SENT TO LOCK YOU INTO THE PACT.

I WAS WAVERING ON THE EDGE OF THAT DECISION!

I WAS SITTING AT THE CORNER OF YOUR BEDSIDE, PONDERING.

BUT I BROUGHT RUBEL TO ME, AND THROUGH HIM I KEPT MY MIND.

YOU ARE ALIVE BECAUSE OF A THIEF, THOUGH HE DOESN'T KNOW IT.

BUT THIS WILL MAKE YOUR JOURNEY DIFFICULT; YOU HAVE BEEN POISONED FOR MANY WEEKS.

THE TEMPTATION TO DIE MAY BE DIFFICULT TO OVERCOME.

BUT FOR THE REST OF YOU...

YOU NEEDN'T WORRY, —LEAVING HERE WILL BE EASY. I NEED ONLY CLOSE THE CIRCLE.

WE ARE HERE, AREN'T WE? I DON'T FEEL DEAD!

WHAT WILL HAPPEN?

HOW..?

YOU WILL EXPERIENCE A MOMENT OF AWARENESS AS YOU TRANSITION, BUT THEN YOU WILL PASS ON.

WE ARE DEAD?

HOLD ON!

BUT THAT CANNOT BE!

QUITE!

OVER THE DUST OF YOUR LONG DEAD BONES, YOUR SPIRITS WILL MAKE THEIR WAYS AS THEY WILL.

BOOM

YOUR BODIES ARE MERELY CONTAINERS.

YOU HAVE GREAT TASKS AHEAD, SO THE LESS FEAR AND REGRET YOU TAKE WITH YOU, THE EASIER IT WILL BE.

BAH! I DON'T BELIEVE YOU. THERE'S MORE TO IT THAN THAT!

I KNOW IT! —THIS IS SOME SORT OF TREACHERY!

THERE IS ONLY OLD TREACHERY.

MY MURDERING YOU MADE ME YOUR JAILER.

AND MY REGULAR VISITS MADE ME YOUR ANGEL AND YOUR RELIEF.

NOW ONLY I HAVE THE POWER TO FREE YOU.

FREE US?

BAH!

I THINK YOU MEAN TO KILL US AGAIN!

—THAT'S WHAT YOU'RE LEADING UP TO, ISN'T IT?!

TO DIE HERE IS TO BE FREE IN A VERY REAL SENSE

BAH

YOU THINK YOU'LL BE TAKING ME WITHOUT A FIGHT?! —I DON'T GIVE A DAMN FOR ALL YOUR MAD EXPLANATIONS!

IF DYING IN BATTLE IS YOUR WISH, I WILL ABIDE BY IT.

BUT YOUR LIFE HERE WILL END, AND I WILL BE THE INSTRUMENT OF IT.

YOU MUST REALIZE THAT THERE IS NO STRUGGLING AGAINST ME. —I AM FINAL.

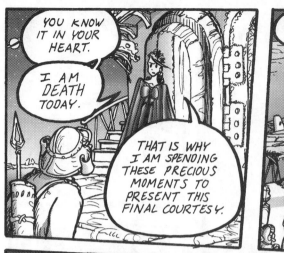

YOU KNOW IT IN YOUR HEART.

I AM DEATH TODAY.

THAT IS WHY I AM SPENDING THESE PRECIOUS MOMENTS TO PRESENT THIS FINAL COURTESY.

—KNOW THIS AS WELL...

I DID NOT TELL YOU THE NATURE OF THIS WORLD BEFORE BECAUSE I WAS SELFISH AND FOOLISH AND I WANTED YOUR COMPANY.

I WANTED YOU AS MY PRISONERS.

FORCED COMPANIONS.

MY MASTER MAY HAVE COMMANDED YOU HERE, BUT I KEPT YOU.

I SHARED YOU WITH THE DRAGON AND WE DRANK YOU UP TOGETHER AND THUS MADE OURSELVES INTO CAPTIVES AS WELL.

THAT TIME IS FINISHED.

I HAVE GROWN UP AND BECOME JUST A LITTLE BIT MORE THAN I WAS.

PERHAPS ONE DAY I WILL BE COMPLETE, I DO NOT KNOW.

BUT TODAY, AN ERA ENDS.

THOUGH...

BEFORE IT DOES, THERE ARE OTHER PACTS I MUST DISSOLVE.

MORTHALANUE!

JALE!

TO ME!

MORTHALANUE AND JALE...

YOUR LONG SERVICE TO MY HOUSE IS NOW OVER. I RETURN THE CLASPS OF YOUR SOULS SO THAT YOU MIGHT BE COMPLETE AGAIN.

YOUR PATHS AND CHOICES ARE NOW YOUR OWN, YOUR TENSIONS ARE RELEASED!

PITY AND GLORY TO YOU FOR THAT!

YOUR LIVES AND TROUBLES ARE ONLY BEGINNING!

AND SO I THANK YOU FOR YOUR LOYAL SERVICE; IT WILL NOT BE FORGOTTEN.

AND IN TIME, IF YOU ARE ABLE TO REMEMBER, EACH OF YOU MAY APPROACH ME ONCE AND REQUEST THAT I GRANT A BOON.

UNTIL SUCH A TIME AS I GRANT YOUR WISH I WILL BE INDEBTED TO YOU.

BUT UNTIL THEN, BE GONE!

I NO LONGER NEED YOU!

I NO LONGER WANT YOU!

FOOF

THE SHADOW SISTER IS HARSH WITH HER SERVANTS.

IT IS SOMETIMES BEST TO BE HARSH.

I DID NOT ASK FOR THEM. —BUT I TOOK THEM ANYWAY.

AND I DEPENDED UPON THEM FAR TOO MUCH.

IT HAS DONE THINGS TO ME I WOULD NOW CHANGE.

PAST NOON!

AUTUMN COMETH...!

I WILL BE MUCH SOFTER WHEN THE TIME COMES TO RELEASE YOU.

BUT I DO NOT WANT FOR SUCH A TIME!

HA! HA!

THAT MAY CHANGE. —YOU DID NOT ASK FOR ME.

YOU HAVE BARELY KNOWN ME A HEARTBEAT. —AND YOU WILL BE LOST FOR A TIME WHEN THIS PLACE ENDS.

I WILL NOT BE LOST!

HA! HA!

WILL SERVE YOU FOREVER!

MM...

I HAVE HEARD THAT BEFORE AS WELL...

HMM...

INDEED.

POF

FFFFT

THERE.

NOW BE GONE WITH YOU AS WELL!

SCURRY BACK TO YOUR MASTER!

OUR PACT IS BROKEN! —IT IS ENDED!

THIS IS THE END!

ALL OF YOU, MY KINGS! QUICKLY NOW!

MAKE YOURSELVES OPEN AT THE DEEPEST LEVEL...!

STAND AND FACE THE ARCH!

UNCLENCH ALL YOUR FEARS AND WOES!

FACE YOUR ADVENTURE WITH EXPECTANT AWE AND CONFIDENCE AS IS FITTING.

THE ARCH IS THE DRAGON'S EYE, AND HE MUST SEE US HERE. HE MUST KNOW IT IS THE END!

GAZE AND LET HIS DAWNING FILL YOU. HE IS BRIMMING WITH THE REALIZATION THAT THE WORLD WITHOUT IS QUAKING AND ALIVE OF ITS OWN SUBLIME ACCORD.

IT IS WAITING FOR HIM TO SHAKE OFF HIS SLUMBER AND JOIN AT LAST WITH THE LIVING!

FEEL HIM RISE!

MAY HIS CHALLENGES BE WELL MET.

HE IS STRONG AND WHOLE NOW AFTER SUCH SLEEP!

AND MAY LUCK BE WITH US ALL, FOR THIS IS THE END OF MY KNOWLEDGE.

AFTER HERE, ALL OLD CHAINS ARE BROKEN AND ALL FORTUNES BORN ANEW!

AT LAST!

Chapter 12

*T*he gun boomed with a deafening report, and the torso of the assassin-sorceress exploded in a horrible shower of warm matter and slithery parts. —All of which would certainly have been more than enough to horrify any but the most stalwart souls, but those present were far too caught up in the flow of thundering events to take much notice. The gruesome detail would have to wait around until it could be properly colored with the correct feelings and emotions; those most appropriate for exploding sorceresses. Battles are often like this; waiting breathlessly for time to catch up.

In the very next fraction of an instant, Rubel, no longer held aloft by his neck, tumbled through the smoke and debris over the edge of the shattered balcony, vanishing at once from view. His trajectory was fast and downward and terminal. —None of which were particularly new for Rubel, but Kimithin had only known him for a short while and she caught her breath sharply. Emotion enough.

An instant later she was streaking across the stones, the leaden weight of the ensorcelled nous-staff forgotten in her hands. Without another thought, she sprang like a small cat over the fallen sorceress and into the blowing ocean of air high above the city.

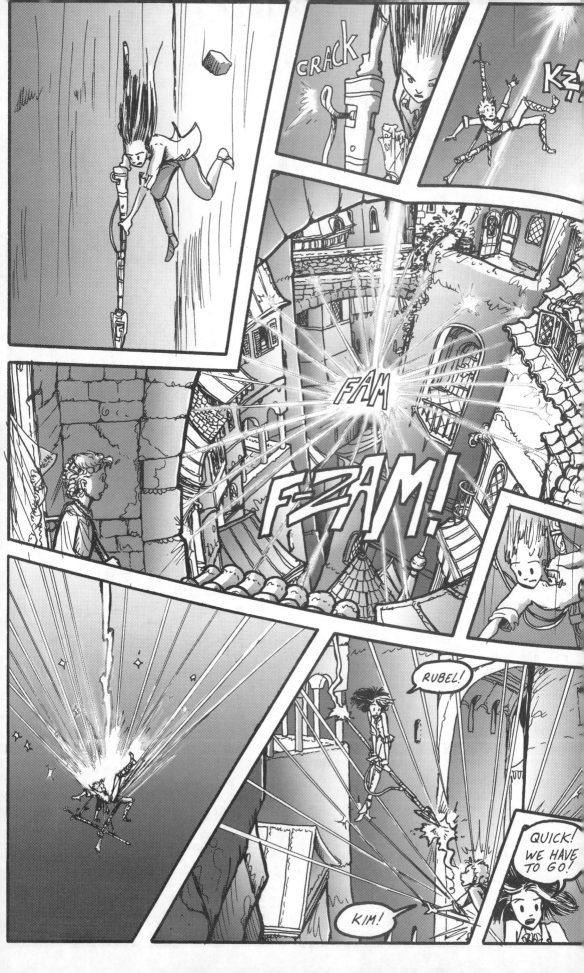

STOP.

YOU STAND IN MY WAY, LUCILLE?

YES, DAMN IT! KIMITHIN AND THE THIEF MUST *LIVE!*

YOU MADE THEIR ESCAPE A PERILOUS ONE, AND THAT IS GOOD, BUT THEY MUST *LIVE!*

ASH IS TOO IMPETUOUS! HE WAS A FOOL TO SEND YOU! YOU ARE TAMPERING IN A DELICATE SPELL.

MY WITCH-CRAFT MUST NOT BE DISTURBED!

SPLTTT

QUEEN SORACIA'S CLOAK HAS JUST ARRIVED WOUNDED AND DISGRACED BEFORE OUR MASTER.

SHE HAS BROKEN HER SWORDS.

WHAT

FOOF!

THE SWORD SHADOWS YOU CONTROL ARE MEANINGLESS NOW.

YOUR WITCHCRAFT IS IN CHAOS.

THE THIEF DIES TONIGHT!

NO!! I PLANNED FO THIS AS WELL

IT IS MO IMPORTANT NOW THAN EV THAT I BE ALLOWED T FINISH!!

NO!

DAN

SHATTER

HEY! I GET IT! I CAN CUT YOU FREE WITH ONE OF THESE!

QUIVER

WHOA!

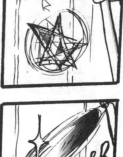

HEA

ZZZT!

ZZT!

SNK

VARKIAS.

GO AND FETCH THOSE POISON NEEDLES YOU HAVE HIDDEN.

—WE'RE LEAVING.

OKAY. HOW DID—

NOW, VARKIAS

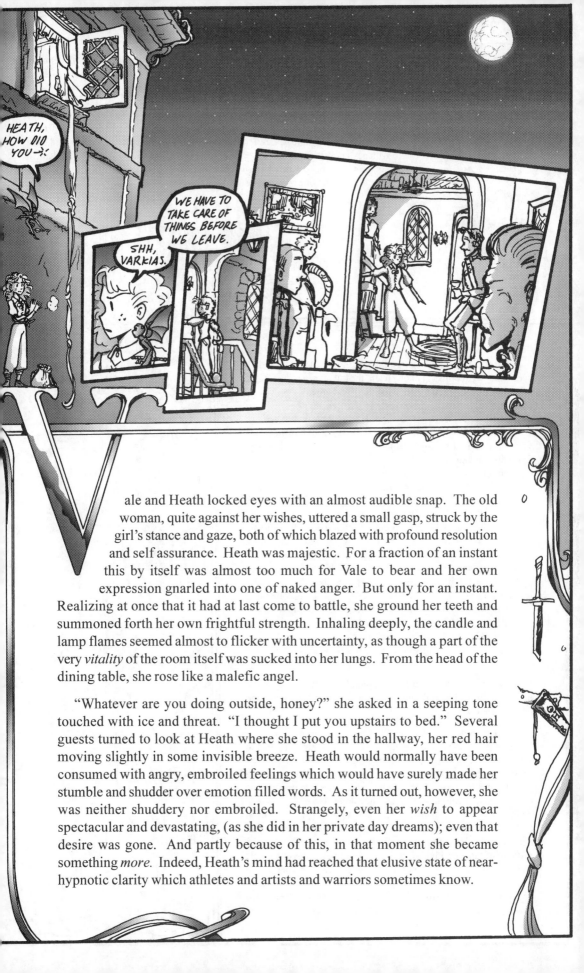

HEATH, HOW DID YOU→:

WE HAVE TO TAKE CARE OF THINGS BEFORE WE LEAVE.

SHH, VARKIAS.

0

Vale and Heath locked eyes with an almost audible snap. The old woman, quite against her wishes, uttered a small gasp, struck by the girl's stance and gaze, both of which blazed with profound resolution and self assurance. Heath was majestic. For a fraction of an instant this by itself was almost too much for Vale to bear and her own expression gnarled into one of naked anger. But only for an instant. Realizing at once that it had at last come to battle, she ground her teeth and summoned forth her own frightful strength. Inhaling deeply, the candle and lamp flames seemed almost to flicker with uncertainty, as though a part of the very *vitality* of the room itself was sucked into her lungs. From the head of the dining table, she rose like a malefic angel.

"Whatever are you doing outside, honey?" she asked in a seeping tone touched with ice and threat. "I thought I put you upstairs to bed." Several guests turned to look at Heath where she stood in the hallway, her red hair moving slightly in some invisible breeze. Heath would normally have been consumed with angry, embroiled feelings which would have surely made her stumble and shudder over emotion filled words. As it turned out, however, she was neither shuddery nor embroiled. Strangely, even her *wish* to appear spectacular and devastating, (as she did in her private day dreams); even that desire was gone. And partly because of this, in that moment she became something *more.* Indeed, Heath's mind had reached that elusive state of near-hypnotic clarity which athletes and artists and warriors sometimes know.

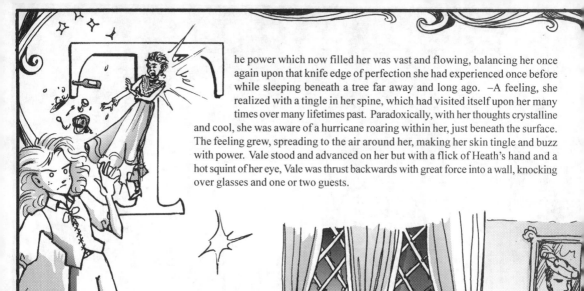

he power which now filled her was vast and flowing, balancing her once again upon that knife edge of perfection she had experienced once before while sleeping beneath a tree far away and long ago. —A feeling, she realized with a tingle in her spine, which had visited itself upon her many times over many lifetimes past. Paradoxically, with her thoughts crystalline and cool, she was aware of a hurricane roaring within her, just beneath the surface. The feeling grew, spreading to the air around her, making her skin tingle and buzz with power. Vale stood and advanced on her but with a flick of Heath's hand and a hot squint of her eye, Vale was thrust backwards with great force into a wall, knocking over glasses and one or two guests.

A current of fear traveled through the room. All were quiet, all eyes clamped unblinking upon Heath, the hot breeze of her magic affecting all, making the guests feel light and unreal. Jenny rose, alarmed.

"Heath? Sweetheart, are you okay? Your arms are bruised. . ."

"I'm okay now," Heath told her. "I just got free from where your mother tied me up. But I'm okay now. Don't worry. Everything is okay now."

"Demon girl!" Vale cried in ice rage, struggling to her feet. "See! Do you see?! I told you all what she was!"

Heath turned and glared back at her, her expression filled with fire. And then, as it was always destined, as Heath *knew* would happen from deep inside those parts of herself where Quinton told her she should look, an instant came when Vale's stubborn, unforgiving train of thought found itself faltering ungracefully for the first time in many years. Her imperious self assurance stopped and asked itself if perhaps Heath might not be something stronger and more dangerous than even she had first suspected; something more than she should ever have been toying with. Her lip twitched, and all at once, she *saw*. A clear flicker of the age and power which lived inside Heath danced now in the girl's eye. —A power far greater than anything Vale kept in the strong house of her own heart.

"Devil girl. . ." she breathed, stepping back, steadying herself on her chair, and then dropping into it as her feet wobbled and became useless.

Heath uttered a short laugh. "You, silly woman. You've hated me from the moment you saw me. —I didn't do anything bad to you. Not once! I've never done anything mean to *anyone* since I came here, but all you've ever done is try to hurt me and make your friends hate me. That's SO dumb! There are people I've never even met who have decided they don't like me! I've seen them down at Zelga's store, talking about me as if I wasn't even there." She breathed deeply through set lips. "—I kept hoping that maybe you'd turn out to like me if I tried hard enough, but you're just one of those stubborn old people. You never in your whole life got up the courage to admit that maybe you aren't perfect all the time. That maybe everybody around you isn't stupid and bad. You never learned how to forgive! Well that's too bad," she intoned darkly, "because now you're going to die."

What little color was in Vale's cheeks faded to nothing. Heath laughed. "No. Not like that. –Though I could. I've finally figured out how." She clenched a hand and felt a living, hot crackle pass through the space within her fist. "But no, you've done it to yourself. When I leave here, you'll be dead in less than a week. You'll die from shame and guilt and all the things you regret in life. I can see it on your face right now! This was your moment, and you didn't even realize how much you were gambling on it. Everything. You didn't leave anything in case you failed. And now you're going to die." She paused briefly, acknowledging the sober victory and all that it entailed. "And all because you and your sister met some pirates on the beach. . ."

Vale quailed at this in shock, her heart pierced through. "No. . !" she cried, her eyes wide in horror. She grasped at the arms of the chair she had fallen into. *"No!"*

Heath huffed at her. "Who *cares* if Jenny's father was a pirate? He was a good man! He would have stayed with you if they weren't going to hang him! And even though he left, he sent plenty of money. More than enough to for you and Jenny to live on forever if you'd spent it wisely. But you didn't." Heath fumed. "You had to *pretend.* You had to keep up *appearances!* And the money all ran out years ago. When what you *really* should have done in the first place was sail away with him. Like your *sister* did!"

"No," Vale croaked, sobbing. "No! *Please. . .*"

But Heath was relentless.

"That day on the beach was a *Magic* day, Vale. It was *full* of power! Your *sister* saw it. She *knew.* And what's so wrong with being a sorceress!?" she demanded, raising her arms. "Why is that so *bad?* But you were too ashamed. And not just because of everything else, but because you knew that you really *did* want to go. You had it all inside you, just as strong as her! You wanted it *so* badly. And you *should* have! You should have gone! Why *didn't* you?" Heath asked, nearly pleading, nearly stamping her foot in frustration. She squinted in fiery thought, and then she knew the name, the details rushing now, filling out in her mind like a living map. "Marthe," she said.

"Except her friends called your sister Marty-Jade, because she was beautiful and magical and fierce. They loved her and they depended on her! She was strong and happy and she left you behind to be bitter when you should have gone *with* her. You're such a fool! I can see it all in your face right now! Your sister had adventures and lovers and people who cared about her and who she cared about. She did all the things you're too stiff and ashamed to admit you wanted. And now you'll never know them! She died full of life, with friends all around her, while your life has been empty and boring and mean. You might have people who *respect* you, but you don't have anybody who *loves* you, Vale. Except for Jenny, but that's only because Jenny is so good. —And its all because you wasted your life crushing down all your dreams so that you wouldn't risk being embarrassed. *Embarrassed!* What a horrible shame! And now you're trying to crush down your daughter's life as well, just to make sure she ends up as miserable as you."

"No. . !" Vale managed to gasp. "Not miserable. I want her to be *safe.* She's not strong enough. . ."

Now Heath did snort. "Jenny's plenty strong. She has a powerful life ahead and she'll live it well. But you would have strangled it out of her if I'd let you. You're supposed to *support* your daughter! Not push her into a weak and frightened life. Well, anyway, it's too late for you. You never learned how to face shame and regret, you've always just pretended it wasn't there. Well, now there's an entire ocean of it inside you, and even though you've been holding it back for fifty years, it's going to gush out all at once and you won't be able to stop it. You'll be dead from regret and sorrow before this week is done. I can see it all over you! I can see it in your *heart*. Maybe in your next life you'll get it right. I hope you do. But in this life, your time is up. And thank goodness! I was really getting sick of you!"

And with that, Vale slumped down listless and broken and Heath turned away, not bothering to spend another atom of attention on her. She turned to face the baffled looking Geof Perkins who, unlike everyone else in the room, really didn't know enough to understand the depth of the blow Heath had served Vale. Geof was young and innocent, and Heath recognized this immediately as well. She spoke his name aloud and Geof made a small swallowing noise in response.

"Um. . , Miss?" he managed.

Heath laughed, but not unkindly, and she looked at him in deep thought for a moment. "You seem like a good person," she said, "I can tell you really do care about Jenny. —I thought before I saw you that you were going to be awful, but you're not so bad," she considered him a moment more and then shook her head sadly. "But I'm sorry. You don't know enough and you're not strong enough. Maybe one day you will be, or maybe you'll meet a girl who's at your level. I don't know. But right now and over the next few years, —which are going to be filled with all kinds of trouble, Jenny is going to need more than you can give her. If you married her, she'd just end up being your mother more than she would your wife, and that wouldn't be good for either of you. She needs a lot more than money; especially when it's money coming from your father. —I don't know what your father is up to exactly, but I can tell just by standing here it has to do with Jenny's job at the royal customs office and to what her husband used to do before he died. —And to the people he used to know. It's all about your dad trying to get more power over people in bad ways."

She turned and glared at Perkin elder, who puffed up at this public disclosure in spite of the instinctive menace he felt pouring from the girl. "I can tell that much just by looking at you!" Heath accused. "Your heart is filled with awful things. You've hurt good people and weaker people in terrible ways, and you'll do it again, I can tell." She scowled at the man and an edge of threat entered her voice which made all in the room shiver, "But you will *not* do it to Jenny."

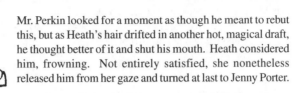

Mr. Perkin looked for a moment as though he meant to rebut this, but as Heath's hair drifted in another hot, magical draft, he thought better of it and shut his mouth. Heath considered him, frowning. Not entirely satisfied, she nonetheless released him from her gaze and turned at last to Jenny Porter.

"Jenny," she said, the strange edge in her voice melting as she looked at the woman who had given her all the warmth and safety she had to give. Jenny, emotional and radiant, her cheeks flushed, took a step forward.

"Oh, Heath."

"I'm sorry," Heath said, her own cheeks flushed. "I'm sorry about your mother. I know you still love her, but she's just not strong or wise enough. There are important things for you in the future, and so this is how it has to be. You'll be much stronger after, I promise. And I also promised Smith Robins; he wanted to tell you that he loves you. He's the one you should marry. Just because he's younger than you isn't a problem. It's okay, and you shouldn't feel guilty. He'll be able to help you with your problems, and he'll do it without hesitating; without a thought for himself. He loves you truly, with his whole heart. Together, you'll be able to fix all the problems you both have and you'll both be very happy. —But he's gone off to do something dangerous. After Geof's brothers beat him up, he made me promise to talk to you and then he ran off."

Jenny reacted to this with a start. "What. . ?" She blinked in puzzlement and looked across at the two brothers. Neither could meet her eye.

"He's gone off," Heath went on. "He was very determined. Smith Robins is the son of a corrupt dutchy in the country side. He wanted to separate himself from his family and to keep it all a secret. I don't know if he's going to make it back alive or not. But if he lives, you must see him again. I know all of this right now by magic, but it's written out for you in a package upstairs. Listen. Out on the rooftop in Rubel's trunk there's a package for you. It's from Mrs. Zelga. Rubel had to go rescue it, but he forgot to tell me that he did. Anyway, it's a pair of woolen mittens wrapped in brown paper. —Mrs. Zelga understands about Smith Robins, except she doesn't like to gossip, so she wrote a note to you in a way which wasn't about him. It's about the mittens you left in her shop last winter." Heath paused and smiled. "It will all make sense when you read her note. Mrs. Zelga is very clever."

enny nodded to all this, only half listening. She knew what was coming next and it made her heart quiver and break inside her. She held out her arms to Heath and clutched the girl's shoulders. Heath allowed herself to fall into Jenny's embrace and the two hugged deeply.

"I'm going now," Heath gasped, stepping back. "Don't worry about me. I stayed living here too long already. I had a vision about it all. . . I have important things that need doing and I have good friends to help me do them. Don't worry about me. I'll come back again sometime to make sure everything is okay. . . I love you."

"Oh, Heath." Jenny felt helpless. It was happening far too quickly. The finality had risen up as though from nowhere, and it was choking her. She cast about. "But do you have everything you need? Everything for going away? Oh honey. . !" She pressed a hand up to her own face, tears standing her eyes. "Do you have proper shoes. . ?"

Heath only smiled at her sadly. Varkias settled on her shoulder carrying a pair of sticky needles tied in leather.

Jenny, one of the few in the world who could see the imp, appealed to him. "You must take care of her," she said, trying to keep her voice from buckling beneath the weight of love and sorrow. "You must! Both you and Rubel! Rubel is a brave boy and he must look after her." She held Heath in her eyes for a long moment more. "She's still so very young. . ."

"We'd both die for her," Varkias said, meaning it very seriously. He understood Jenny's love. "We'll take care of her. I promise."

And so, with the watching audience of simple men and women standing in their finest evening clothes, dazed far beyond their normal lives, and with the summer evening air smelling sweetly outdoors, Heath and Jenny hugged once more and kissed each other goodbye. Then with light steps which made almost no sound, Heath Wingwhit turned and walked out the door.

She walked from the house like a flicker of candle light, moving through the shadows until she had faded into the city night, vanishing as though she had never been in Jenny's house at all.

Epilogue

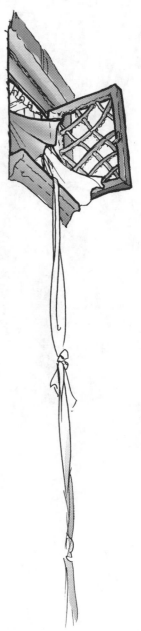

QUINTON?

CAREFULLY NOW. —YOU'RE NOT QUITE WHOLE YET.

WHERE AM I?

WE THOUGHT YOU HAD LEFT US, LADY.

WE WERE VERY SAD.

WE ARE SO VERY PLEASED YOU LIVE!

BACK OFF, YOU BRUTES!

LET HER BREATHE!

SHE'LL HAVE TIME FOR YOU WHEN SHE'S RECOVERED!

WE RODE TO PALVINCIA TO FIND YOU.

KING RILLION?

WE HAD TO FIGHT OFF LOCUMIRE'S HORRORS, I CAN TELL YOU!

THEY WERE INTENT ON TAKING YOU!

THANK YOU, QUINTON.

BUT YOU KNOW THIS DOESN'T MEAN I'M GOING TO JUMP INTO WHATEVER SCHEME YOU HAVE PLANNED FOR THE WORLD.

—I'M NOT ABOUT TO SELL MYSELF AGAIN AFTER FINALLY ⁓

OH NO! DON'T EVEN THINK IT!

I WOULDN'T DO THAT!

HONESTLY! WHAT DO YOU THINK I AM?

I'M ACTUALLY VERY PROUD OF YOU.

YOU?

YOU'RE PROUD OF ME.

WELL, YES! —YOU'VE COME SUCH A LONG WAY.

OH, SALLY...

I KNOW YOUR PATH HAS BEEN DIFFICULT.

AND YOU'LL STILL HAVE TO WORK TO MAINTAIN YOUR WILL... —WHAT WITH THAT PIECE OF MY BROTHER'S HEART STILL INSIDE YOU...

BUT AFTER ALL YOU'VE DONE, IT WILL BE SO MUCH EASIER.

SALLY, YOU DID SO WELL!

YEAH...

TEN-THOUSAND YEARS HAS A WAY OF AFFORDING SOME SKILL.
—MY CLOAK WAS THE THING I WAS REALLY WORRIED ABOUT.

BUT I DIDN'T WAVER AT ALL.

YOU DID WONDERFULLY.

I'M VERY, VERY PROUD.

Last Page of the Story.

Ahh. Welcome to the tail end of this book. I don't know about you, but it took me nearly three years get here!

This book was very satisfying to complete. In particular, I was very pleased to be able to devote so much time to Quinton, (who I find balances out Soracia's melodrama quite nicely). And while I wasn't able to give Heath or Rubel quite as much time to themselves as I had wanted, what can one do. . ? I realized several years ago that I was far more in service to the story than the other way around. . .

Nonetheless, in the next volume I plan to give more time and space for growing up to Heath and Rubel and his new friend, (girlfriend?). I have it all set in my mind's eye, and I know all sorts of exciting and dramatic things which will happen for them.

Oh, you'll see. . .

One of the larger questions in my mind, though, is this: What of Quinton? You may have noticed that over the past four books, I've endeavored to keep him either asleep or locked up or packed away in entirely different periods of history where he can do relatively little damage. Quinton is rather like an unexploded, inter-dimensional chaos bomb, and he scares the willies out of me. As a writer who likes to make sure all the chess pieces and back drops and various nooks and crannies are all organized nicely, when I think of the sorts of things Quinton is capable of doing on a whim. . . Well, let's just say that the instant you drop somebody like Quinton into a city like Oceansend, all bets are off.

The problem is that Locumire and the prince really *are* getting very powerful, and the universe has a way of seeking balance. . .

Whatever happens, I'll be certain to make room for my favorite characters to be themselves and enjoy their time with each other. —So long as I'm in charge around here!

Take care!
—Mark Oakley

The End